Horse and Rider

Asking them the question!

Horse and Rider

1000
QUESTIONS AND ANSWERS
FOR HORSEMEN

By HARRY DISSTON

Illustrated by PAUL BROWN

New York: A. S. Barnes and Company

London: Thomas Yoseloff Ltd

A. S. Barnes and Company, Inc.
8 East 36th Street
New York 16, N. Y. 10016

Thomas Yoseloff Ltd
18 Charing Cross Road
London W.C.2, England

6131
Printed in the United States of America

NOTE

In general, an answer is considered correct only when it is expressed essentially—not necessarily exactly—as given in the Answer Section. Where questions involve approximations with respect to figures, a variation of 5 per cent is generally considered correct, except with respect to the height of horses in which case the variation should not exceed 1 inch. Where specific items are called for, however, the answer is considered correct only if the specific number of items is stated. For example, if the answer to "Name three breeds of draft horses" includes only two, it is considered incorrect. There should be no fractional scorings, each answer, in conformity with the preceding statements, being considered correct or incorrect.

To the many horses, horsemen, and horsewomen who helped—
directly and indirectly—to produce this book

PREFACE

THIS BOOK I HOPE MAY PROVE INTERESTING, ENTERTAIN-
ing and perhaps informative to those who in one way
or another enjoy a horse. It may in some instances also
provide the stimulus for an increase in knowledge and
consequently the enjoyment of that splendid animal.

In separate sections will be found questions, answers and
a table for determining on a percentage basis the number
of questions answered correctly. With the thought that it
may make this fireside and easy chair sport more interesting, and more effectively to evaluate the score obtained, the
average scores of representative small groups—from com-
parative novices to experts—are shown at the head of each
section of the questions. These "average" scores should not,
however, be considered as standard due to the very small
sample and to the geographical proximity of those tested.

The questions were compiled with a view to covering a
range broad enough to be interesting and informative in
varying degree both to the novice and to the experienced
horseman. The questions were selected with the further
thought that the answers would include largely the sort
of general information that one well acquainted with the
subject covered in a particular section would be apt to

know. Expressed mathematically, it was intended that among a representative group of horsemen generally considered well qualified in their respective fields, the majority would answer correctly from 85 to 95 per cent of the questions, while a novice would average only about 20 per cent.

The reader will, I am sure, appreciate the scope and natural limitations of this type of book. It is not intended to be a technical treatise; the answers are not exhaustive nor do they in general go beyond a suitable and accurate response to the specific question. Where questions pertain to the height, weight, performance, characteristics, action desired, etc., the answers are based on the general or average under usual conditions. To have done otherwise would have meant an exhaustive treatment which is beyond the scope of this book and would confuse its purpose. Controversial subjects were avoided as far as possible.

Each answer has been carefully checked with sources of reliable information reflecting:

1. The facts determined from reliable available records, or

2. The published regulations or rules of recognized governing bodies, adhering to the national organization when both national and local associations govern a field, or

3. The opinions of recognized authorities in their respective fields, or

4. In some cases, personal experience.

In addition each section has been reviewed by a recognized authority in that field. Technical terms were avoided in the answers with the thought that thus the book would be more interesting to the relatively uninformed and in some instances to avoid giving the clue to another answer.

May the reader have as much fun using this book as I had preparing it.

H. D.

Hidden Hill Farm
Shadwell, Virginia

CONTENTS

CONTENTS

General and Historical

AVERAGE SCORES:
(Per cent answered correctly)

5 who do not ride or own horses	21
5 who ride but do not own horses	44
5 who ride and own horses	70
3 veterinary surgeons	82
3 United States Cavalry officers	83

To determine your score (or anyone else's), count the number of questions answered correctly and consult the table on pages 225 and 226.

The answers to the questions in this section will be found following the list of questions, on pages 22 through 29.

GENERAL AND HISTORICAL
QUESTIONS

1. What are the unmixed colors of horses? (Start with the darkest.)

2. What is a piebald?

3. What is a skewbald?

4. What is a roan?

5. What is the correct term for what is sometimes referred to as a "sorrel"?

6. What, with respect to a horse's markings, is a race?

7. What is meant by "hogging"?

8. What is meant by "docking"?

9. In what unit of measurement is a horse's height expressed?

10. How many inches are contained in this unit?

11. What, approximately, is the height of a small horse (e.g. a polo mount)?

12. What, approximately, is the height of a large riding horse (e.g. a hunter)?

13. What, approximately, is the weight of a small horse (e.g. a polo mount)?

14. What, approximately, is the weight of a large riding horse (e.g. a hunter)?

15. What, approximately, is the weight of a draft horse?

16. What weight is the English "stone"—in pounds?

17. What is a normal male horse called?

18. What is a female horse called?

19. What is a gelding?

20. What are newly born horses—without regard to sex—called?

21. What are newly born male horses called?

22. What are newly born female horses called?

23. How long does a mare carry her young?

24. What does the average Thoroughbred foal weigh at birth?

25. At what age, approximately, are foals weaned?

26. What is meant by an "aged" horse?

27. What is the normal life span of a horse?

28. What, according to available records, is the longest a horse has lived?

29. Approximately how far can a conditioned horse under average favorable conditions of footing, country and weather, be ridden in a day without exhaustion?

30. Approximately what is the length of a running horse's stride?

31. What are the fastest three gaits, in order of speed?

32. What is the highest a horse has jumped?

33. What is the farthest a horse has jumped—the broad jump record?

34. Which is the "near" side of a horse?

35. What is the other side called?

36. Riding cross-country you come to a stream; would you allow your horse to drink?

37. Returning to the stable after a long ride, what would you do with respect to unsaddling?

38. What precaution should be taken when approaching a horse from the rear?

39. What do historians generally accept as the first use made of the horse by man?

40. What is the name of the horse usually associated with Alexander the Great?

41. What is the name of the horse usually associated with Napoleon?

42. What is the name of the horse usually associated with the Duke of Wellington?

43. What is the name of the horse usually associated with Robert E. Lee?

44. What is the name of the horse usually associated with George Washington?

45. What is the name of the mythological winged horse?

46. What is the generally accepted theory as to the origin of the horse?

47. What is the generally accepted theory as to the first appearance of the horse in North America?

48. Name three distinctly American breeds of horses.

49. Name three breeds of riding horses, not included in the answer to the preceding question, that are used in the United States.

50. Name two breeds of light harness horses.

51. Name three breeds of draft horses.

52. Which breed of draft horse was most common in the United States?

53. What is a "cob"?

54. What is a "mustang"?

55. What is a "broom tail"?

56. What is an ORLOFF?

57. What is a PALOMINO?

58. In round numbers, about how many horses are there in the United States?

59. What is a common misuse of the term "Thoroughbred"?

60. What are the chief characteristics of the THOROUGH-BRED?

61. What are the chief characteristics of the MORGAN?

62. What are the chief characteristics of the ARAB?

63. What is the origin of the HACKNEY?

64. What are the chief differences between the WELSH and the SHETLAND pony?

65. Which is the oldest of the improved breeds of horses used today?

66. What is the sire of a mule?

67. What is the dam of a mule?

68. Name three characteristics of appearance distinguishing the mule from the horse.

69. What is a HINNY?

70. What relation, if any, is the zebra to the horse?

71. Will an offspring result from the mating of the horse and the zebra?

72. What is an ONANGER?

73. What is a KIANG?

74. What is the height of the tallest known horse?

75. Express, as an approximate percentage of his own weight, the weight a good draft horse can pull?

76. Express, as an approximate percentage of his own weight, the weight a good Shetland pony can pull.

77. Who was Rosa Bonheur?

78. What is characteristically incorrect in the representation of horses depicted in motion prior to about 1850?

79. When a horse rises from lying down, which legs are up first?

80. What is meant by a "cold blooded" horse?

GENERAL AND HISTORICAL

ANSWERS

1. Black, brown, bay, chestnut, dun, light gray (the usual manner of referring to a white horse)—with, of course, varying shades of these.

2. A black and white horse, the white patterned in big splotches or patches on the black, or the reverse.

3. A horse whose coat is patched BAY, CHESTNUT or BROWN and white—as distinguished from a piebald, which is black and white.

4. A horse whose color is made up of chestnut, brown, red, or bay, thickly interspersed with white.

5. A light chestnut.

6. A narrow stripe down the face, usually in the center.

7. Clipping the mane close to the neck.

8. Cutting the tail, usually very short.

9. In "hands" and inches.

10. Four inches.

11. 14.3 to 15.2 hands. The average is probably 15 or 15.1.

12. 16 to 17 hands. The average is probably 16.2.

13. 900 to 1,100 pounds. The average is probably 1,000.

14. 1,150 to 1,350 pounds. The average is probably 1,200.

15. 1,600 to 2,400 pounds. The average is probably 1,900.

16. 14 pounds.

17. A horse or stallion.

18. A mare.

19. A castrated horse.

20. Foals.

21. Colts.

22. Fillies (Singular: Filly).

23. Eleven months.

24. About 120 pounds. They generally range from 90 to 140 and on occasions even up to 160.

25. At about six months.

26. One exceeding *nine* years of age. (Some, but I don't agree, say eight).

27. From twenty to twenty-three years.

28. The greatest age attained by a horse, according to available records which are reasonably authentic, is 53. Clover, the property of the Rev. Dr. Uriah Myers of Catawissa, Pa., is known to have been that old—or possibly a year or two older—when he died in 1924. Old Bill who died at Washington, N. J., in 1925 is reported—but less reliably—to have been 55 at that time. It is claimed that an English draft horse, "Billy," had reached the great age of 63 when he died in 1822.

29. Approximately forty-five miles. This distance was actually averaged by the United States Cavalry over a three weeks' period, foraging on the country. This, however, is frequently exceeded. In the annual endurance tests in Vermont, the horses, largely Morgan stock, were ridden an average of 60 miles for five days. On two occasions at the

United States Cavalry School at Fort Riley, Kansas, a squadron of cavalry with full pack equipment has been marched 100 miles in twenty-four hours (eighteen hours actual marching) and gone on the next day for several miles without the loss of a horse. In peace time, a day's march for conditioned cavalry mounts, with full equipment, is generally thirty-five miles.

30. From the time any hoof leaves the ground until that hoof strikes again, from 20 to 26 feet.

31. The (extended) gallop; the pace; the trot. (The "canter" is a collected gallop).

32. 9 feet, 6 inches. BEN BOLT accomplished this at the Royal Horse Show in Sydney, Australia, in 1938. Fred Wettach's KING'S OWN cleared 8 feet, 3½ inches in November 1925.

33. Over 39 ft., allegedly by Chandler in 1847, in Warwickshire, England. More recently, in September 1933, Master Crump ridden by Larry Lansburgh jumped a distance of 36 feet over brush and water at San Mateo, California, equaling two previous jumps of the same distance by Louie Leith's Roustabout and Julian Morris' Overall at Laurel, Md. Nigra, a United States Army mount, jumped 35 feet clearing triple bars and Touraine, another army mount, jumped 33 feet.

34. His left side.

35. The "off" side.

36. Yes. There is no harm in a horse drinking moderately even if he is hot—not overheated or in a lather, however—provided he is moved along directly after drinking. There is an ill effect only if he is allowed to stand.

37. Leave the saddle on for a time, then loosen the girth, so that the blood will not too suddenly return to the long-compressed blood vessels under the saddle.

38. Speak to him in a calm voice so that he will not be startled and perhaps kick.

39. To draw war chariots; low, two wheeled affairs of narrow trace.

40. Bucephalus.

41. Marengo.

42. Copenhagen.

43. Traveler.

44. Nelson.

45. Pegasus.

46. That he is descended from a small cleft hoofed quadruped, reaching its present characteristic development in Asia.

47. While fossil remains indicate that, in prehistoric times, horses existed in the North American continent, probably by successive migrations from Asia, the entire race became extinct. The horse was re-introduced, through Mexico, by the Spaniards, who brought horses with them from Europe, on their voyages of exploration—the first by Cortez in 1519.

48. The Standard Bred (American Trotting Horse); The (gaited) American Saddle Horse; The Morgan Horse; The Tennessee Walking Horse; The Quarter Horse; The Palomino; The Appaloosa.

49. Thoroughbred; Arab; Half Bred.

50. Hackney and Standard Bred.

51. The breeds are: Shire, Belgian, Clydesdale, Percheron, Suffolk.

52. Percheron.

53. A small, short-legged, stocky horse, with a high stylish action, used generally for driving, but frequently for riding.

54. A small, hardy, half-wild horse, native to the southwestern United States and Mexico.

55. A small, wild horse, not worth taming, found in rapidly decreasing numbers on the plains of the western United States.

56. A light harness breed (trotting horse) native to and popular in Russia. From the stud of Count Orloff, it is derived from a mixture of Arabian, Dutch and Frisian blood.

57. A horse colored three shades lighter or darker than a newly minted gold piece, with a flaxen mane and tail. The breed is registered as to color only.

58. There appear to be between 2 and 3 million. Exact figures are not available. The estimate is based on information from the U. S. Department of Agriculture and the records of the several breed registries.

59. It is commonly misused for pure bred; such as reference to a "thoroughbred" saddle horse or "thoroughbred" Morgan, when "pure bred" is intended.

60. Extreme refinement of form and appearance, thin skin, a long slender neck, small head and ears, uniform coloring; he is extremely fast, and possesses staying power and courage to a high degree.

61. All around usefulness, endurance, and consistent perform-ance; he is easy to keep, and docile. He has smooth lines, stylish action, little speed; small ears, fine eyes, a crested

neck; characteristically he is 14.3 to 15.1 hands high and weighs 1,000 to 1,200 pounds.

62. Endurance, ability to subsist on scanty food and little water. He is small, higher at the croup than at the withers; has a finely-shaped, small head and small ears, coarse hocks. He has one vertebra less, and his tail is set slightly higher, than other breeds.

63. In England, of composite blood, from Norfolk trotters— sired by Thoroughbreds out of Dutch mares in Norfolk and neighboring counties in England. The foundation sire was Blaze, a Thoroughbred; the dam, a cold blooded Norfolk hunting mare. Their get, the Shales Horse, was foaled in 1760.

64. The Welsh pony is larger, has shorter hair and possesses more nearly the quality of a Thoroughbred.

65. The Thoroughbred.

66. An ass (Jack).

67. A mare.

68. Its (a) longer ears, (b) rat tail, (c) smaller, narrower flinty hoof, (d) straight back, (e) thicker neck, (f) proportionately bigger head, and (g) straighter pasterns.

69. The offspring of a stallion and a jennet (female ass).

70. It belongs to the same family.

71. Yes. The offspring of a zebra and a mare is called a zebrass.

72. A small, wild, fleet footed ass inhabiting the deserts of Asia from Syria and Persia to India and Mongolia.

73. A wild ass inhabiting the high isolated regions of Tibet, in the vicinity of lakes and streams.

74. 20 hands (6 feet, 8 inches); a Suffolk, "Pat," owned by R. J. Connor of Phelps, N. Y.

75. 50 to 75 per cent. A half to three quarters of its own weight; e.g. a 2,000-pound draft horse can pull 1,000 to 1,500 pounds, ½ to ¾ of a ton.

76. 100 to 150 per cent. Usually up to half again its own weight; e.g. a 400- to 500-pound Shetland can pull 500 to 800 pounds.

77. A well-known woman painter of animals, especially horses, in motion. Her "Horse Fair" painted in 1853 (or 1855) is famous.

78. They are pictured running like dogs, fore and hind feet extended, like this:

A horse galloping actually looks like this:

79. The FORELEGS.

80. One that is not a Thoroughbred.

Anatomy and Stable Management

P.B.

AVERAGE SCORES:

(Per cent answered correctly)

5 who do not ride or own horses	12
5 who ride but do not own horses	29
5 who ride and own horses	62
3 United States Cavalry officers	94
3 veterinary surgeons	100

To determine your score (or anyone else's), count the number of questions answered correctly and consult the table on pages 225 and 226.

The answers to the questions in this section will be found following the list of questions, on pages 40 through 48.

ANATOMY AND STABLE MANAGEMENT
QUESTIONS

On the sketch below point out the following:

1. Poll.
2. Withers.
3. Throat latch.
4. Point of the shoulder.
5. Hock.

6. Forearm.
7. Fetlock Joint.
8. Pastern.
9. Loins.
10. Crest.

On the sketch below name the parts indicated by:

11. "A."	14. "D."	18. "H."
12. "B."	15. "E."	19. "I."
13. "C."	16. "F."	20. "J."
	17. "G."	

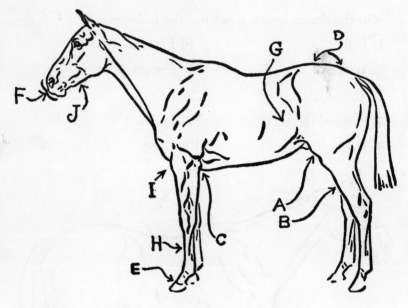

21. What are the elongated callouses (horny structures) on the inner surface of a horse's legs called?

22. Are the chestnuts above or below the knees?

23. Are the chestnuts above or below the hocks?

24. What is the chief characteristic of good shoulders for a riding horse?

25. What is the chief characteristic of good pasterns for a riding horse?

26. What is a tendon?

27. What is a ligament?

28. How many ribs has a horse?

29. What is the number of foal teeth?

30. How many teeth has a mare?

31. How many teeth has a horse?

32. What is Galvayne's Groove?

33. About how old is a horse whose teeth look like this?

34. About how old is a horse whose teeth look like this?

35. About how old is a horse whose teeth look like this?

36. About how old is a horse whose teeth look like this?

37. What are wolf teeth?

38. What, normally, is the youngest age at which all of the milk teeth have disappeared?

39. Name the principal joints in the foreleg.

40. Name the principal joints in the hindleg.

41. Into what three major parts is the hoof divided?

42. Why is exercise necessary to stimulate the condition of a horse's feet?

43. What characteristic of a horse's stomach is important in considering the frequency of feeding and the quantity of a "feed"?

44. What are "cow" hocks?

45. What is meant by "ewe necked"?

46. What is meant by "sway-backed"?

47. What is meant by "tied in below the knee"?

48. What is meant by "splay-footed"?

49. What is meant by "herring-gutted"?

50. What is meant by "Roman nosed"?

51. What is meant by "dishing" or "paddling"?

52. What is meant by "brushing" or "interfering"?

53. What, in addition to a proper diet, does a horse require to maintain good condition?

54. Name three foods, other than hay and oats, important in a horse's diet.

55. Which is generally considered the best hay in the United States for riding horses?

56. What are the characteristics of good oats?

57. How is a bran mash made?

58. Name a food for horses high in fat, heat and energy producing properties.

59. Name a food, or constituent of foods, high in bone making properties.

60. Why is it not well to use hay for bedding?

61. What besides straw makes good bedding for horses?

62. In what order is a horse given grain, hay and water?

63. About how often a day should a horse which is working be fed?

64. About how many quarts of oats a day should be fed a riding horse of medium height and weight which is getting an average amount of work?

65. About how much hay a day?

66. About how much water should a horse drink a day?

67. If you desired to reduce the amount of oats in a horse's diet and replace them with hay, what rule of thumb would indicate the amount of hay to substitute?

68. What is the chief contribution of hay to the diet?

69. How may the tendency of some horses to bolt their food be corrected? Name two methods.

70. What is the result of a horse's overeating when grazing if he is not accustomed to grass?

71. What measures, in general, would you take to bring a horse in poor condition to good condition, where there is no specific ailment?

72. How would you determine that a horse had been properly groomed?

73. What disease is apt to affect a horse's hoof if it is not kept clean?

74. Name three stable vices.

75. Name three precautions to prevent sore backs.

76. Where should a curry comb *not* be used?

77. What is the usual manner of feeding salt?

78. What is a twitch?

79. From the ground to what part of its body is a horse's height measured?

80. What are the usual dimensions of a box stall?

ANATOMY AND STABLE MANAGEMENT
ANSWERS

1.
2.
3.
4.
5.
6.
7.
8.
9.
10.

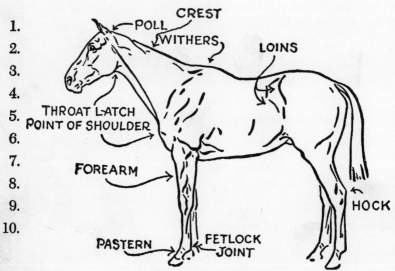

11. Stifle.
12. Gaskin.
13. Elbow.
14. Croup.
15. Coronet.
16. Muzzle.
17. Flank.
18. Cannon.
19. Arm.

20. Bars of the jaw.

21. Chestnuts.

22. Above.

23. Below.

24. That they be sloping, at approximately a 30-degree angle from the vertical, and have low points.

25. That they slope at an angle from the vertical of approximately 45 degrees in the forelegs and 30 degrees in the hind. If they are short and straight, the horse's gait will be choppy and uncomfortable; if they slope too much or are too long, the horse's legs will be weak.

26. An inelastic fibrous cord or band, attaching a muscle to a bone, transmitting the force of the muscle to it.

27. Inelastic (generally), tough, fibrous tissue, which binds bones together to form joints.

28. 18 pairs; 8 pairs of "true" ribs and 10 pairs of "false" ribs.

29. 24.

30. 36 (and occasionally 38).

31. 40 (and sometimes 42).

32. A well defined groove close to the gums on the upper corner incisor teeth which extends gradually downward with advancing years. Useful in determining a horse's age.

33. 8 years.

34. 21 years.

35. 4 years.

36. 14 years.

37. Small rudimentary teeth which sometimes appear in front of the first molars on the upper jaw. They interfere with the action of the bit and should be removed.

38. At five years of age.

39. The shoulder, elbow, knee, fetlock, pastern, and coffin (inside the hoof).

40. The hip, stifle, hock, fetlock, pastern, and coffin.

41. The wall, the sole, and the frog.

42. Because only by pressure, and the release of this pressure on the frog, is blood circulated through the hoof; in short it is the only means of keeping the hoof in condition and nourishing it.

43. It is very small and there is no gall bladder; food does not stay in it long, and when about two-thirds full, the food is forced out of it at about the rate it is consumed. It is therefore important to feed frequently, in small quantities.

44. Hocks turning or bending inward so that the cannon bones and joints of the hocks are unusually and abnormally close together.

45. When the top line of the neck is distinctly concave—a neck that appears to be put on upside down. This:

46. A back that is hollowed, forming a "saddle" between the withers and croup. Like this:

47. When the back line of the tendon noticeably converges inward toward the knee. This:

48. Refers to feet that turn out (Toeing out). This:

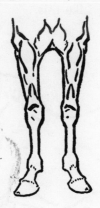

49. When the underline of the belly cuts sharply upward toward the rear (Light waisted). This:

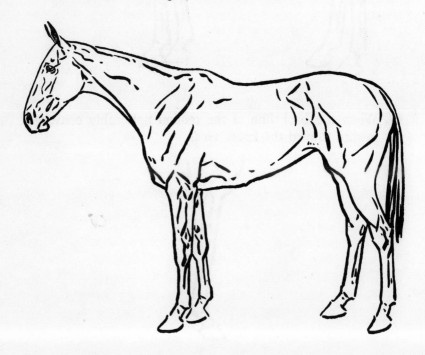

50. A convex face with the muzzle rounding decidedly downward. Like this:

51. Swinging the forefeet sideways when trotting.

52. The interference of the inner portion of a hoof with the opposite leg (fore with fore or hind with hind) so as to cause abrasions, cuts, or other injuries.

53. Regular exercise and grooming.

54. Greens, corn, bran. Other foods are: barley, wheat, rice, millet, rye, beans, peas, linseed, carrots, and potatoes.

55. A mixture of upland timothy with clover and some alfalfa.

56. They should be plump, short, hard, of a uniform size, clean white in color, and weigh not less than 38 pounds to the bushel; they should rattle when dropped on a solid, hard surface; they should be odorless, break sharply across when bitten, and taste like good oatmeal.

57. By steeping several pounds of bran in as much boiling

water as will be absorbed, stirring it well, adding a pinch of salt, and allowing it to steam until it is cool enough to eat. Sometimes an equal quantity of oats is mixed with the bran and also steamed.

58. Corn; and in lesser degree, rice and millet.

59. "Salts": alfalfa, meadow hay, clover hay; all have the necessary high calcium content.

60. Because it is apt to be eaten.

61. Sawdust, shavings, sand (except in damp or cold climates), peat moss and pine needles.

62. Water, hay, grain.

63. Three times at least, and, in the case of large horses and "big feeders," four or five times are even better.

64. About ten quarts (or pounds); from nine to twelve.

65. About ten pounds; from nine to twelve.

66. About eight gallons; depending upon the temperature and amount of work, this will vary from five to fifteen gallons. When plenty of water is available, horses should of course be allowed to drink all the water they wish, so long as it is not within an hour after feeding.

67. Three pounds of hay for each pound of oats.

68. It provides the bulk or "filler," minerals and vitamins.

69. (a) Include a proportion, not exceeding ten per cent., of chaff (loose stems, leaves, flowers, seeds, etc.) with each feed; or (b) spread the feed out thinly over a large surface; or (c) place several bars over the top of the manger to divide it into compartments; or (d) place a few large stones or other bulky non-edible substance in the feed.

70. Flatulent colic is an almost certain result, especially if the

grass is wet or frosty.

71. Give him a physic ball; increase and graduate the amount of regular exercise and food, progressively over a long period; and groom thoroughly each day.

72. Run the fingers through the coat against the natural lay of the hair, pressing firmly against the skin. If the horse has not been properly groomed, flakes of dandruff and lines of grey will appear on the horse's coat, and the tips of the fingers will be covered with scurf. Also look under the crown piece of the halter, below the ears, under the belly, on the inside of the forelegs and thighs, and in the bends of the knees and hocks—regions often slighted.

73. Thrush or canker.

74. The most usual are: weaving, wind-sucking, cribbing (gnawing the woodwork), biting, kicking against the stall, tearing blankets, halter pulling, and eating dung.

75. The most important are: The use of a properly fitting saddle; proper placing and adjustment of the saddle; sitting properly in the saddle and not unduly shifting the weight (not slouching, sitting on the cantle, standing in one stirrup, etc.); keeping the under side of the saddle clean; dismounting occasionally on long rides to lead or rest; not removing the saddle too soon after hard work; maintenance of good condition in the horse.

76. Not on the legs, from the knee down, and not on the head.

77. In cakes or bricks of rock salt placed in the manger, or "licks" in a special container on the wall near it.

78. A small piece of rawhide or rope passed through a hole in the end of a stick of wood about 2½ feet long and 1½ to 2 inches in diameter—used to restrain a horse by twisting the thong about his upper lip.

It looks like this:

Is used like this:

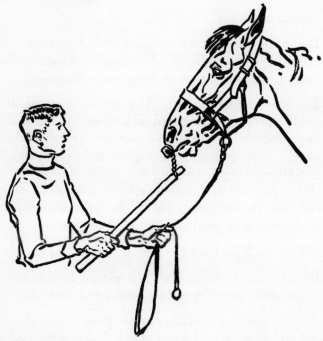

79. The withers.

80. 10 to 12 feet square.

First Aid and Shoeing

AVERAGE SCORES:
(Per cent answered correctly)

5 who ride but do not own horses.	17
5 who ride and own horses.	46
5 who operate their own stables.	85
5 livery stable proprietors.	84
5 U. S. Cavalry officers.	90

To determine your score (or anyone else's), count the number of questions answered correctly and consult the table on pages 225 and 226.

The answers to the questions in this section will be found following the list of questions, on pages 56 through 65.

FIRST AID AND SHOEING

QUESTIONS

1. How might a horse's manger indicate the horse is sick?

2. Name the three types of lameness.

3. How is lameness, not readily evident, best determined?

4. How would lameness in a FORELEG be indicated?

5. How would lameness in a HINDLEG be indicated?

6. How would you test for SHOULDER lameness?

7. Is the seat of lameness found more often in the fore or hind legs?

8. What is a "BLISTER"?

9. Name the basic ingredients of the two most common types of blister.

10. Name ten essential medicines usually included in a stable first-aid kit.

11. What part of a horse's body is affected by THRUSH?

12. What causes it?

13. What is the most usual cause of CORNS?

14. Of CONTRACTED HEELS?

15. What part of the horse's body is affected by LAMINITIS?

16. Name THREE causes of the disease.

17. What are the major symptoms?

18. What is another, common, name for Laminitis?

19. What part of the horse's body is affected by a CURB?

20. How should it be treated?

21. How should a BOWED TENDON be treated?

22. What is STRINGHALT?

23. What part of a horse's body is affected by QUITTOR?

24. What is the blemish known as a "FEATHER"?

25. Distinguish between RINGBONE and SIDEBONE.

26. Distinguish between a SPLINT and a SPAVIN.

27. What is the distinction between BOG SPAVIN and BONE SPAVIN?

28. What is PINFIRING?

29. What is meant by "stifled"?

30. How should saddle sores be treated?

31. What is the normal protection for overreaching?

32. Name a simple solution to kill lice.

33. An excessive amount of what food in the diet may cause pimples and fistules to appear on the horse's body?

34. Name three uses commonly made of belladonna.

35. Is coughing a disease?

36. What change of diet may cause coughing?

37. Is STRANGLES more common in young or old horses?

38. What is the purpose of a mallein injection?

39. Name three antiseptics used on horses.

40. Name two purgatives for horses.

41. What is the composition of a common poultice?

42. What is the composition of white lotion?

43. For what purpose is SALTPETER (Potassium nitrate) used?

44. What is COLIC?

45. What is the first-aid treatment for COLIC?

46. Name the composition of a common COLIC tonic?

47. Name the two common types of colic.

48. What is a SITFAST?

49. What is the normal pulse rate (number of beats per minute) of a horse?

50. What, approximately, is the horse's normal temperature?

51. Where is a horse's pulse taken?

52. Where is a horse's temperature taken?

53. To what part of the body does CONJUNCTIVITIS pertain?

54. To what part of the body does OPHTHALMIA pertain?

55. To what part of the body does MEGRIMS pertain?

56. To what part of the body does THOROUGHPIN pertain?

57. What is the usual remedy for CRIBBING?

58. In destroying a horse, where should he be shot?

59. What should be done with a horse coming in exhausted or overtired by hard work?

60. How would you treat a common cut?

61. How many nails are in the normal shoe?

62. What is a CALK?

63. What is a QUARTER CLIP?

64. Name the blacksmith's essential tools.

65. What is meant by pathological shoeing?

66. Name the first of the five major steps in shoeing a horse. (Omit removing the old shoe.)

67. Name the second of the five major steps in shoeing a horse.

68. Name the third of the five major steps in shoeing a horse.

69. Name the fourth of the five major steps in shoeing a horse.

70. Name the fifth of the five major steps in shoeing a horse.

71. What is meant by "cold" shoeing?

72. What is the difference between the shoes on the fore and on the hind feet?

73. Name three essential features of correct normal shoeing.

74. How often, as a rule, should a horse's shoes be changed?

75. If at the normal time for reshoeing, the shoes are very little worn, what, if anything, should be done?

76. How many sizes of standard commercial shoes are there for light horses?

77. What is the most common result of poor, faulty, inexperienced, and careless shoeing?

78. Name the shoe illustrated. What is its use?

79. Name the shoe illustrated. What is its use?

80. Name the shoe illustrated. What is its use?

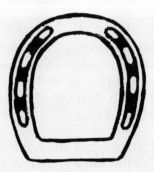

FIRST AID AND SHOEING
ANSWERS

1. By a quantity of uneaten forage. The manger is normally clean after each feeding.

2. (a) Supporting-leg lameness, caused by disease or injury of the bones, tendons, ligaments and foot.

   (b) Swinging-leg lameness, caused by disease or injury of the muscles.

   (c) Mixed lameness, caused by a combination of the preceding and by disease or injury of the joints.

3. By slow trotting the horse on a loose lead rein toward and away from the observer, if practicable, on an up-and-down grade and by turning the horse at a walk and trot. The horse should be "cold."

4. The stride is shortened and the horse's head bobs up and down noticeably. The head rises when the affected foot touches the ground; contact of the affected foot with the ground is relatively light and of short duration and it is carried well forward and planted well in advance of the sound foot. The sound foot is then quickly planted, to relieve the weight on the affected foot.

5. The stride is shortened and the head bobs up and down as in lameness of the foreleg, and in addition the croup rises with the affected hindleg and drops with the planting of the sound hindleg. The head acts opposite to its action

in forefoot lameness, the head now being *down* when the affected foot strikes the ground.

6. Pull the horse's leg forward, then backward, as far as it will go, several times. If he flinches or tries to rear, lameness in the shoulder is indicated. If he is now trotted again he will go more lame than before. Walk or trot the horse over a bar; it will drag the lame leg.

7. The fore.

8. A counter-irritant causing inflammation of the skin, rubbed on the affected part to draw the blood to that area and thus speed recovery.

9. (a) Cantharides (Black blister or Spanish Fly).
   (b) Biniodide of mercury (Red blister).

10. Most of the following would be usual:

Alcohol	Linseed oil
Aloes	Lysol
Alum	Methylene blue
Ammonia, spirits	Oil of turpentine
Antiphlogistine	Peroxide
Belladonna extract	Pine tar
Bichloride of mercury	Potassium bromide
Biniodide of mercury oint-	Potassium permanganate
ment	Silver nitrate
Boracid powder	Sugar of lead (white lo-
Carbolic acid	tion)
Cantharides ointment	Sulphur ointment
Colic mixture	Vaseline
Creolin	Witch hazel
D. D. T.	Zinc oxide
Fever mixture	Zinc sulphate
Iodine	

11. The FROG of the hoof.

12. Wet, dirty and badly drained stalls; standing or traveling a long time in mud and water and, of course, infection.

13. Improper shoeing which allows the sole to rest on the shoe, or leaving shoes on too long—and bruises.

14. Improper shoeing, continued use of calks, causing lack of frog pressure; permitting shoes to remain on too long; undue cutting away of the bars of the frog; lack of exercise.

15. The FOOT—usually one or both of the front feet.

16. Sudden chilling from standing in a draft; drinking large amounts of cold water when hot; over-eating of grain; eating improper or spoiled forage; over-exertion, exhaustion.

17. Sudden intense lameness in the forefeet—and sometimes all four. The forefeet planted in advance of the body and the hindfeet well forward under the belly. The horse is difficult to move or turn. Accelerated pulse and respiration; high temperature; heat in the affected feet.

18. FOUNDER.

19. The HOCK.

20. Rest the horse. Apply cold water packs to the curb; apply iodine or antiphlogistine. Blister if necessary.

21. Treat in the same manner as a curb.

22. A nervous disorder which causes a horse suddenly to snatch up one or both hindlegs, especially when first taken from the stable or backed.

23. The HOOF (the lateral cartilages).

24. A white scar on the cornea of the eye.

25. RINGBONE is a bony enlargement of the pastern joint, usually near the coronet. SIDEBONE is a bony growth on the lateral cartilage causing a bulge on the side of the coronet.

26. A SPLINT is a bony enlargement along the union of the splint and cannon bones, characterized by a localized bulge or swelling on the inside (generally) or outside of a fore or hind leg, more usually the fore, between the knee or hock and the fetlock. A SPAVIN is a disease affecting the bones of the hock joint, characterized by a swelling on the inner and lower part of the hock.

This is a splint: This is a spavin:

Splint →

Spavin →

27. BOG spavin is a distention of the hock joint capsule—a puffy swelling on the inside and a little to the front of the hock. BONE spavin is a *bony growth* inside and just below the hock.

28. Applying internal heat by puncturing the skin with fine pointed needles heated red hot in a fire, or special lamp. This treatment is used frequently in the reduction of serious cases of curb, spavin, splint, ringbone and bowed tendons.

29. Lameness produced by the "knee cap" (patella) on the front or inside of the stifle joint being displaced.

30. Wash them with a mild disinfectant and warm water, then apply boracic powder or white lotion. Do not saddle the horse until the sores have healed. Most important, remove the cause.

31. Quarter boots or other felt or leather protection covering the fetlock joint. It can usually be prevented by corrective shoeing.

32. D. D. T., or creolin or carbolic acid (a tablespoonful) in a pint of water. Six ounces of tobacco, boiled in a gallon of water for 20 minutes is also effective—but it must be used sparingly and not more than once in 24 hours, to avoid nicotine poisoning.

33. Corn.

34. (a) To relieve pain in the eye and dilate the pupil;
    (b) To relieve the pain and spasms of colic; and
    (c) For sprains.

35. No. It is a symptom of various diseases.

36. The change from grass to grain. (It is also caused by dusty hay.)

37. Young horses.

38. To test for GLANDERS.

39. They include: alcohol, metaphen, methylene blue, merthiolate, and iodine.

40. Aloes (ball), linseed oil, mineral oil and epsom salts are most usual.

41. Flaxseed or linseed meal and bran stirred in hot water until thick and pasty and a little lysol or carbolic acid—also, antiphlogistine.

42. Sugar of lead (lead acetate) and zinc sulphate, a tablespoonful of each, in a quart of water.

43. Internally with water, for the treatment of fevers and laminitis and as a diuretic; externally, as a cooling lotion in the treatment of sprains and bruises.

44. A stomach ache—from a variety of digestive disturbances, ruptures, twisted intestines, etc.

45. Place the horse in a large, well bedded stall. Administer a colic drench. Roll up a hot blanket and apply under the belly, well back. Call a veterinarian. Do not feed for at least 12 hours.

46. Most common is:
    Oil of turpentine (2 tablespoonfuls) in
    Linseed oil (1½ pints) and
    Whiskey or brandy (2 tablespoonfuls)
  Another is:
    Aromatic spirits of ammonia (2 tablespoonfuls)
    Extract of belladonna (1 dram in a pint of water)
  A third, frequently used, is:
    Camphor gum (6 tablespoonfuls)
    Carbolic acid (2 tablespoonfuls)
    Glycerine (12 tablespoonfuls—12 ounces)

47. (a) FLATULENT (wind colic) and (b) SPASMODIC.

48. A small patch of hard, dry, dead skin or scab on a horse's back, covering a saddle sore.

49. 36 to 40.

50. 100° Fahrenheit.

51. Under the jaw in front of the large cheek muscle (the submaxillary artery)—on either side, but usually on the near side.

52. In the rectum.

53. The eye.

54. The eye.

55. The brain.

56. The hock.

57. (a) Remove as many projections in the stall as practicable and creosote the edges of the remainder.

(b) Fasten a strap about the horse's throat just tight enough to compress the larynx when the horse presses with its teeth.

58. In the forehead, above the level of the eyes under the forelock, at the intersection of lines connecting the base of each ear with the opposite eye. Here:

59. Place a bucket of tepid water in its stall; give it a little hay but *no* grain; massage its legs and back. Be sure there is ample clean bedding. When the horse is rested, feed a bran mash.

60. (a) Clean with a warm antiseptic solution (lysol, 2 table-spoonfuls in a pint of water or 1 part of hydrogen peroxide to 5 parts of water).
    (b) Apply iodine (tincture).
    (c) Dust with boracic powder twice daily
    or,
    after cleaning, apply sulfanilamide powder.

61. Generally 7 and only occasionally 8; 4 on the outside and 3 on the inside, when there are 7.

62. A protrusion (or, sometimes, a dull spike) at the toe and the heel ends of a shoe to prevent slipping. It is generally made by bending the ends down. This is a calked shoe:

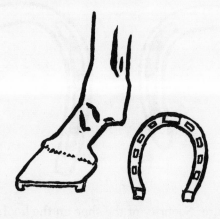

63. An upward bend of the metal at the forward sides of the shoe (usually the hind) to increase the security of its attachment to the hoof and minimize loosening from scuffing and stumbling.

64. Anvil, vice, hammer, tongs, knife, rasp, pincers, pritchel and buffer.

65. Shoeing to correct or relieve deficiencies of gait, movement or conformation, disease and lameness.

66. Prepare (trim) the hoof.

67. Make the shoe.

68. Fit the shoe.

69. Drive the nails.

70. Finish the shoe.

71. Nailing on a prepared shoe, fitted in advance or of a standard size, without heating or fitting it.

72. Shoes on the forefeet are rounder at the toe, wider and shorter than those on the hindfeet and seldom have calks.

This is a *fore* shoe:　　　This is a *hind* shoe:

73. Essential are: Security of the shoe on the hoof; correct nailing; maintenance of the natural level and alignment of the foot; provision for expansion of the foot; prevention of sole pressure. Most important, that the smith fit the shoe to the foot and not vice versa.

74. Every 4 to 5 weeks.

75. The shoes should be removed, the hoof trimmed and the shoes reset.

76. Four: Numbers 0, 1, 2 and 3.

77. Corns and contracted heels are common; injuries due to improper placement of nails; in some instances, navicular disease.

78. A FEATHER EDGED (bevelled) SHOE, used to reduce the risk of brushing (interfering).

79. A THREE QUARTER SHOE, frequently used after the removal of a corn.

80. A BAR SHOE, used to relieve pressure on affected parts of the hoof and to provide frog pressure, especially in the treatment of corns, cracked hoofs and contracted heels.

Tack and Equitation

AVERAGE SCORES:

(Per cent answered correctly)

5 who do not ride or own horses	14
5 who ride but do not own horses	47
5 who ride and own horses	72
5 National Guard and Reserve Cavalry officers	86

To determine your score (or anyone else's), count the number of questions answered correctly and consult the table on pages 225 and 226.

The answers to the questions in this section will be found following the list of questions, on pages 76 through 85.

TACK AND EQUITATION

QUESTIONS

1. What is the cantle of the saddle?

2. What is the pommel?

3. What is the tree?

4. What is the name of the small flaps near the pommel, covering the stirrup leathers and bars?

5. Name the two general types of saddles commonly used in the United States.

6. What is a Balding girth?

7. What is a Fitzwilliam girth?

8. What is a roller?

9. What is a surcingle?

10. What is a cooler?

11. What is a cavesson?

12. What is the purpose of the chin strap?

13. What is meant by hook billets?

14. What are the distinguishing features of the Pelham bit?

15. What is meant by a port in reference to bits?

16. What is a double bit?

17. What is a "gag"?

18. What is the correct term for "snaffle"?

19. What is the correct term for "curb"?

20. What is the usual slang term for stirrups?

21. On what items of a horse's equipment are stable or other colors usually displayed?

22. What two parts should be unfastened before removing a Pelham or double bit bridle?

23. What parts of a Pelham bridle should be checked for proper adjustment?

24. Tell the usual difference between the snaffle and curb reins attached to a Pelham bit.

25. Approximately what is the weight of an adult's English (flat) saddle, with girth, stirrup leathers and irons?

26. For what purpose are Pariani saddles generally considered particularly desirable?

27. Name the activity for which this type of flat saddle is primarily designed.

28. This one?

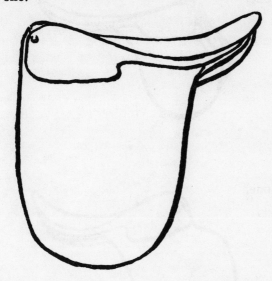

29. This one?

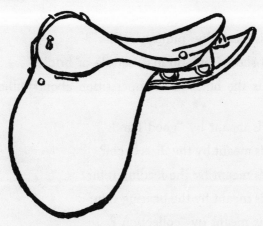

30. This one?

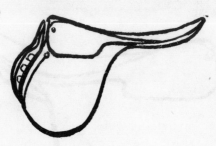

31. This one?

32. What is meant by "pulling leather"?

33. Which should one do first, saddle or bridle?

34. What is the horseman's superstition about pulling on his boots?

35. What is meant by "good hands"?

36. What is meant by the direct rein?

37. What is meant by the leading rein?

38. What is meant by the bearing rein?

39. What is meant by "collection"?

40. What is meant by "two-tracking"?

41. What is meant by taking the track to the right in a riding hall or ring?

42. What are the aids?

43. In a turn to the right on the haunches (quarters), which leg (aid) is used most vigorously and furthest back?

44. In a turn to the left on the forehand, which leg?

45. What is meant by the rider changing "diagonals"?

46. What is meant by a "right lead"?

47. When is a horse said to be "up to the bit"?

48. When is a horse said to be "behind the bit"?

49. What is faulty with respect to the position of the rider's legs and feet in this sketch?

50. To the doctrine of which foreign school of equitation was that taught at the United States Cavalry School most similar?

51. What is a "running walk"?

52. What is a "fox trot"?

53. What is a "rack"?

54. What is a "single foot"?

55. What is the rhythm (number of beats in a full cycle) of the walk?

56. Of the trot?

57. Of the gallop?

58. What is the order in which the feet strike the ground at a walk? Begin with the right hind foot.

59. What is the order in which the feet strike the ground at a trot?

60. At a gallop?

61. When pacing?

62. When a horse lands properly after jumping an obstacle, in what order do his feet touch the ground?

63. What are the chief characteristics of the forward seat?

64. What is meant by "flexion"?

65. What is meant by "high schooling"?

66. If you are swimming a horse on which side should you swim?

67. If a horse "pecks" what do you do?

68. When four reins (two sets) are used, should the curb reins generally be held on the inside or the outside?

69. What should one do with regard to a horse's head when going down a steep hill?

70. What gaits do the following hoof prints indicate?

71. These?

72. These?

73. What is meant by "longeing"?

74. What is characteristic of the seat at the slow trot?

75. What do you do at the riding hall command "change hands"?

76. In what part of the ring do you ride if you are galloping?

77. What should you do if someone behind you says "track, please"?

78. If you wish to adjust equipment, halt, or dismount, in the ring, what should you do first?

79. Name the primary objectives of a good "seat" on the horse.

80. Name THREE items based on which you would judge a rider's proficiency in equitation at the walk (i.e. things you would look for if you were judging an equitation class).

TACK AND EQUITATION
ANSWERS

1. The raised rear part.
2. The raised forward part.
3. The frame over which the saddle is built; generally it is made of wood with some metal reinforcement.
4. The skirts.
5. The English or "flat" (in a number of modifications for a variety of purposes from park riding to high jumping and polo); and the stock or western saddle (with several variations, such as the Whitman saddle, used by the New York City police, and the McClellan saddle).
6. One with the central portion composed of three interlaced straps.
7. One with a thinner strap superimposed on the larger main girth.
8. A cloth band, passed about the horse's body over the blanket at about the spot the middle of the saddle rests, used to hold the blanket in place.
9. A cloth or leather band passing over a saddle or blanket to hold it fast.
10. A thin, generally wool, blanket, used to cover horses while walking to "cool" them, after strenuous exercise such as polo or racing.

11. A noseband used in training horses, especially useful for longeing; also a halter with such a noseband; or a noseband used as part of a bridle to which the upper end of a martingale is attached.

12. To hold the curb chain in place along the chin groove and prevent it riding up on the sensitive jaw bones.

13. Metal fasteners for bridle leather in the shape of hooks, used instead of buckles.

14. The curb and snaffle are in effect combined in one bit, which looks like an elongated letter H; rings, to which the reins are buckled, are attached to the bit (the cross bar) and lower ends of the shanks.

15. It is an elliptical, semi-circular or inverted U-shaped hump in the middle of the bit, to make it more severe and to discourage the horse putting its tongue over it.

16. Two separate bits, the curb and snaffle, as opposed to a "four ring" or Pelham bit, or a curb or snaffle alone.

17. A type of snaffle bit supported from a pulley or through which the reins pass so that when pressure is exerted, the bit rises in the horse's mouth.

18. Bridoon.

19. Bit.

20. Irons.

21. Brow bands, blankets, and coolers.

22. (a) The curb chain and (b) the throat latch.

23. (a) The bit, (b) curb chain, (c) throat latch and, if used, (d) the cavesson noseband.

24. The snaffle reins are slightly wider (about an ⅛ inch) and are fastened by a buckle. The curb reins are sewn together.

25. Approximately 15 to 18 pounds.

26. For jumping especially, and hunting, and often for general riding by those riding the forward seat.

27. Polo and hunting.

28. The show ring (Saddle horses).

29. Military, officers' saddle (Saumur).

30. Flat racing.

31. Jumping.

32. Holding on to the saddle to maintain one's balance or seat, especially when a horse gets out of control or acts in a spirited manner.

33. Bridle.

34. That the LEFT boot should always be pulled on first; to do otherwise will bring bad luck.

35. A light constant contact with the horse's mouth, giving a maximum control of the horse while he remains calm, with the least possible effort or exertion on the part of the rider.

36. The use of the rein in such a way as to place tension to the rear; also known as the rein of opposition. This:

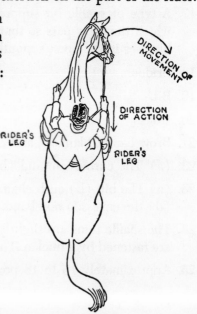

DIRECTION OF MOVEMENT

DIRECTION OF ACTION

RIDER'S LEG

RIDER'S LEG

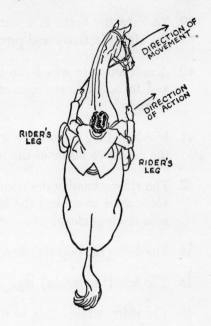

37. The use of the rein, opened out, in a manner to lead the horse's head and neck to the right or left, by carrying the hand to the right or left. This:

38. The use of the rein in a manner to act toward the opposite side of the horse's neck, without increased tension to the rear. For example, the right bearing rein is produced when the right rein (without increased tension to the rear) acts toward the left against the right side of the horse's neck. Like this:

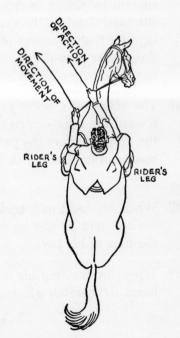

39. To have the horse in a state of proper balance to answer the aids effectively and promptly.

40. A movement in which the horse gains ground to the front and to one side simultaneously without turning his neck or body.

41. Moving along the outside oval or circle of the hall, so that the center or inside of the hall is on the rider's right.

42. The rider's hands (the reins), legs, weight (balance), and voice used to control the horse; sometimes used to designate the legs alone.

43. The left (i.e. outside) leg.

44. The left (i.e. inside) leg.

45. The rider, when rising to the trot (posting), changing his rhythm by sitting or rising an extra half beat, so that he sits (and rises) on the opposite diagonal pair of the horse's legs, for the purpose of relieving one "diagonal" of bearing the greater part of the work, to exercise the opposite diagonal, and to produce a helpful variety.

46. The action of a horse galloping in which he is balanced toward the right—his right forefoot being the last to leave the ground before the period of suspension. He appears to reach out or "lead" with his right, as against his left, forefoot.

47. When his head and neck are in correct position (direct flexion) and he can be controlled by the reins acting on the bars of his jaw.

48. When, by bending his neck, opening his mouth, or both, horse deliberately slackens the reins and thereby severs

the communication between his mouth and the rider's hand. Until it can be forced forward by vigorous use of the legs and again takes hold of the bit, the rider has lost control through use of the reins.

49. The foot is too far forward, the straight leg throwing the body out of perpendicular balance and causing the seat to be insecure. The knee should "cover" the toe. The heel should be down, lower than the toe, but without unduly straining the ankle. The toe should also be turned slightly outward. The ball of the foot should rest on the stirrup. This is the idea:

50. Saumur (French).

51. A gait which is a cross between a walk and a trot.

52. An easy gait in which the steps are very short; a kind of jog, the horse's feet being manipulated as if he were changing from a walk to a trot.

53. A gait in which the lateral legs move almost simultaneously, the hindfoot striking the ground slightly before the forefoot.

54. A gait in which the hindfeet move as in a fast walk, and the forefeet as in a slow trot; each foot strikes the ground singly so that one and two feet are alternately on the ground.

55. Four.

56. Two, and a period of suspension.

57. Three, and a period of suspension.

58. The right hind, the right fore, the left hind, the left fore. Alternately two or three feet are on the ground at the same time; the feet are raised successively and planted in the order in which they are raised.

59. The right hind and then the left fore almost simultaneously; the left hind and the right fore, almost simultaneously; as the horse springs from one diagonal pair of legs to the other, all his feet are off the ground.

60. The right hind; the left hind and right fore almost simultaneously; the left fore, followed by a period of suspension when all feet are off the ground. In this instance the horse would be on a left "lead."

61. Right hind and right fore simultaneously then, following a period of suspension, the left hind and left fore simultaneously. As the horse springs from one lateral pair of legs to the other, all his feet are off the ground.

62. One forefoot touches the ground first (for example, the left—if he is on the right "lead"), then the right fore, followed by the left hind and then the right hind.

63. An alert attitude and a *balanced* position at all gaits over the horse's center of gravity, resulting in the rider "sitting" close to the pommel of the saddle, his weight largely supported by the stirrup irons, and, at gaits faster than the walk, bending forward from the hips, the position of the legs remaining unchanged with the knee "covering" the toe.

64. Relaxation of the muscles of the jaw and poll in yielding to the hand of the rider. The horse's muzzle should not be drawn back so that his face passes the vertical.

65. A system of training movements in which the horse's gaits are shortened and raised.

66. On the down stream side, so as not to be carried against the horse by the current.

67. Let him have his head so that he may see what he is doing and regain his balance. Do not "pick him up" with the reins. The horse uses his head and neck as a counter-balance.

68. On the inside.

69. Steady his head with the reins but do not hold it up unnecessarily. The horse uses his head as a balance pole. Sit perpendicular to the saddle and do not slouch back.

70. A gallop.

71. A trot.

72. A walk.

73. Training or exercising a horse by causing him to move in circles about the trainer on the end of a long rein ("longe" or "longe line or rope") at the various gaits. A long whip urges the horse on.

74. The rider "sits" instead of posting or rising to the trot.

75. (a) Continue to the end of the ring, (b) turn half about and cross to the diagonally opposite corner, and (c) turn half about to continue in the *opposite* direction. Thus the rider(s) change from taking the track to the left to taking the track to the right or vice versa, without decreasing the gait or pace. This is how it works:

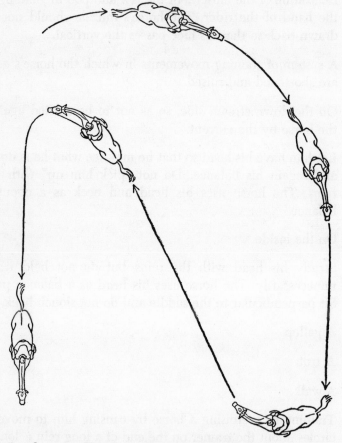

76. On the outside—along the knee boards.

77. Give way by moving toward the center of the ring to let him pass between you and the knee boards.

78. Ride to the center of the ring.

79. (a) Control of the horse; (b) security of the rider; (c) flexibility (making use of all of the joints); (d) a balanced load on the horse's back; (e) comfort and ease of the rider.

80. (a) Position of the body.
   (b) Position and use of the legs.
   (c) Position and use of the feet.
   (d) Position and use of the hands.
   (e) Manner of holding the reins.
   (f) Balance.
   (g) Control of the horse.

Horse Shows

AVERAGE SCORES:
(Per cent answered correctly)

5 who do not ride or own horses but have attended at
   least 3 horse shows   18

5 who ride but do not own horses   32

5 who ride and own horses   59

5 members of recognized Horse Show Committees   89

To determine your score (or anyone else's), count the number of questions answered correctly and consult the table on pages 225 and 226.

The answers to the questions in this section will be found following the list of questions, on pages 97 through 104.

HORSE SHOWS
QUESTIONS

1. What are the gaits of a three-gaited horse?
2. What are the gaits of a five-gaited horse?
3. What class of horse is usually referred to as a "walk, trot"?
4. Name four of the sections in the Saddle Horse Division.
5. How many Pony Divisions are there, excluding "Polo Pony"?
6. What is a hackney?
7. Name three of the usual types of classes for harness horses or ponies.
8. What are the events of Combined Training Events?
9. What is meant by a "registered" horse?
10. What constitutes a novice horse?
11. What is the usual distinction between a horse and a pony?
12. What is a green hunter?
13. What is a qualified hunter?
14. What are the qualifications for a horse "suitable to become a hunter"?
15. What is the distinguishing characteristic of a lightweight hunter?
16. What is the distinguishing characteristic of a heavyweight hunter?
17. What is a Corinthian class?
18. Name five characteristic qualities which may be considered in judging hunters.
19. What is the distinction between a hunter and a jumper?

20. What is this
obstacle called?

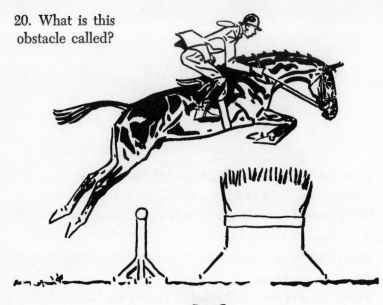

21. This one?

22. This one?

23. This one?

24. This one?

25. This one?

26. This one?

27. This one?

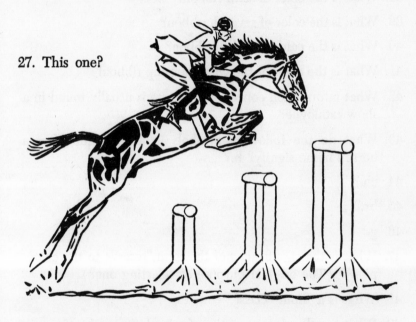

28. Where the difference is scored, is a touch or a knockdown with the forelegs or the hind legs considered the greater fault?

29. What circumstances constitute a fall for a horse?

30. In jumping classes, which refusal causes elimination?

31. In jumping classes what is the penalty for jumping an obstacle before it is reset?

32. What is the penalty for failure to keep to the proper course?

33. What is a Bonus Point Class?

34. What is an "open" jumping class?

35. What are the features of the event known as "The Scurry"?

36. What is the color of fourth ribbon?

37. What is the color of fifth ribbon?

38. What is the color of sixth ribbon?

39. What is the color of seventh ribbon?

40. What is the color of eighth ribbon?

41. What is the color of the championship ribbon?

42. What information concerning a horse is usually found in a show catalogue?

43. What do the following symbols in a catalogue after a horse's name signify? b.?

44. ch.?

45. br.?

46. g.?

47. What is the significance of the term "reserve to the champion"? (The original purpose of selecting one?)

48. What is a "limit" class?

49. What are the characteristics of a "stake" event?

50. What is the meaning of "dressage"?

51. What is a "gymkhana"?

52. Who is an "amateur"?

53. Does the receipt of a cash prize in a horse show classify the winner as a professional?

54. Which is generally considered the most important horse show in the United States?

55. Which is generally considered the most important horse show in the Middle West?

56. In the Far West?

57. Which is considered the most important horse show in the South?

58. Which is considered the most important horse show in Canada?

59. Which is considered the most important horse show in England?

60. Which is considered the most important horse show in Ireland?

61. What equestrian event is included in the Olympic Modern Pentathlon?

62. What are the chief equestrian events included in the Olympic Games?

63. Has the United States ever won an equestrian championship in the Olympic Games?

64. Name four events in the National Horse Show important in encouraging the horsemanship of children.

65. What is the usual upper age limit for "children's" classes?

66. In the event of a jump off over triple bars, how is the obstacle altered?

67. By what established code of rules are military jumping classes in the National Horse Show governed?

68. In computing points for a championship, what values are given the various ribbons?

69. Since World War II, how many foreign countries have been represented by teams in the National Horse Show?

70. Has the United States Team ever won the International Challenge Trophy (team) at the National Horse Show? If so, when?

71. What is the name of the governing body of horse shows in the United States?

72. What is a "Local Show" as defined by that body?

73. In which direction, normally, is an oval or a circular course jumped?

74. What is the name of the two-wheeled vehicle to which hackney's are usually shown?

75. How many classes of recognized Judges are there?

76. What are the qualifications of a Registered Judge?

77. Of a Recorded Judge?

78. In how many different divisions are Judges accredited?

79. Name eight of these divisions.

80. If, in an equitation class, two contestants "in the ribbons" appear to perform equally well, what is the usual procedure for attempting to determine which is the better?

HORSE SHOWS

ANSWERS

1. Walk, trot, canter.

2. Walk, slow gait (running walk, fox trot or stepping pace), trot, canter, and rack.

3. The three-gaited saddle horse.

4. The sections are: Breeding, Three-gaited Saddle Horse, Five-gaited Saddle Horse, Fine Harness Horse, Saddle and Fine Harness Pony, American Saddlebred Pleasure Horse, Saddle Type Horses and Ponies, Western Equipment.

5. Three. They are: Harness Pony Division, Shetland Pony Division, Welsh Pony Division.

6. The outstanding breed of fine harness horse, originated in England late in the eighteenth century. The horse is heavy in proportion to its height but varies considerably in height from a small pony to a 16 hand horse, has a deep chest, heavy croup and quarters, is predominantly of a dark color, has characteristically a high action and exhibits a fine quality.

7. There are classes for (1) single horses and (2) pairs of various heights shown to (3) tandem, (4) phaeton or (5) gig; (6) for ponies, and (7) mares, (8) geldings, and (9) stallions; for (10) novices, and (11) limit classes.

8. Dressage, Competitions in the Open (cross-country galloping and jumping), and Jumping (in an arena).

9. A horse whose name, identity, and number are recorded in the recognized stud book of any country for his particular breed.

10. A horse which has not won *three* first ribbons at recognized shows in the particular division in which it is shown, previous to the show in which it is entered.

11. A horse is over 14.2 hands in height; a pony 14.2 and under.

12. A hunter type horse which has not been hunted with a recognized pack of hounds for more than one season or which has not won a first prize in a hunter class at a recognized show prior to the year in which it is shown, other than in certain hunter classes where the jumps do not exceed 3 feet 6 inches.

13. A hunter type horse which within two years has been regularly hunted with a recognized pack of hounds for more than one season, as evidenced by a certificate from the Master of a recognized Hunt to that effect.

14. A hunter type horse which has not reached 5 years of age and which has not won a first ribbon in a hunter class at a recognized show other than in a green or "suitable" class.

15. One capable of carrying up to 165 pounds to hounds.

16. One capable of carrying up to 205 pounds to hounds.

17. A class open to qualified hunters ridden by amateurs, who are members of (or regular subscribers to) recognized Hunts, in their appropriate Hunt livery. Personal appointments, equipment, and dress are considered in the judging.

18. (1) Conformation; (2) manner and safety of jumping; (3) way of going between jumps; (4) uniformity of pace; (5) manners.

19. A *hunter* should exhibit that he is a safe and sure jumper

over the type of obstacle actually met in the hunting field, that he can gallop comfortably at a uniform pace and in good control and that he is tractable and has good manners; these features are judged by his manner of jumping, his way of going at a gallop, especially from one jump to another, and, very important, his conformation. A *jumper* is required only to clear satisfactorily the obstacles prescribed, usually artificial ones not met in the hunting field, such as triple bars. The manner and way of going over the obstacles, the approach to them or between them, and conformation are given no consideration. The judging is entirely mathematical on the basis of ticks, knockdowns, refusals, etc.

20. Oxer.

21. Hogback.

22. Chicken coop.

23. Liverpool.

24. Aiken fence.

25. Double oxer.

26. In and out.

27. Triple bar.

28. With the forelegs.

29. When a shoulder and a haunch touch the ground, or the obstacle and the ground.

30. The third.

31. Elimination.

32. Elimination.

33. In the Jumper Division, a more than usually challenging

course, providing greater reward for more difficult competition. It is required to have a minimum of 12 obstacles, two changes of direction, specified numbers of obstacles of minimum heights, combinations and spreads. Six ribbons are awarded with show championship points of 7, 5, 4, 3, 2, 1.

34. One in which performance only is considered.

35. It is a jumping event against time over a variety of obstacles, in which only the speed of completing the course and clearance of obstacles is considered. The horse completing the course (usually 8 obstacles) in the shortest time, plus faults (one second added for each fault) is the winner.

36. White.

37. Pink.

38. Green.

39. Purple.

40. Brown.

41. Blue, red and yellow.

42. Its name, color, sex, height, age, registered number (if any) and owner.

43. Bay.

44. Chestnut.

45. Brown.

46. Gelding.

47. The term, now used to indicate runner-up to the champion, originated from the practice current some time ago of

requiring a veterinary surgeon to attest the soundness of the horse judged the champion. In order to avoid the embarrassment of the adjudged champion being found unsound, a second horse was chosen in "reserve."

48. A class open to horses which have not won six first ribbons in the division in which they are shown.

49. One in which the sum of the nominating and entry fees and any added amounts is awarded the winner, and winners of the lesser awards in decreasing proportion; usually limited to horses shown in other similar classes which are not stake events.

50. A test or exhibition of a specified series of training movements, which the horse should execute while appearing "light" in the hands of the rider while also possessed of impulsion and a willingness to obey the slightest command. In its most advanced application, it is the ultimate objective of the horse's high schooling.

51. A contest consisting of one or more mounted events, the winning of which depends largely upon the skill of the rider, such as "musical chairs," a "bending" race, a "Gretna Green" race, a "potato spearing" race, "bareback jumping," etc.

52. Broadly, anyone under 18 years of age, or who does not engage in horse activities either as a means of support or as a method of increasing personal income in any material degree. Such activities include breeding, training, boarding, buying, selling, riding, driving, instructing—or managing a stable or horse establishment or accepting employment in connection with them—or permitting the use of one's name or photograph in connection with horse activities.

53. In equitation classes, where the *rider* is judged, YES. In

classes where the horse is judged and the rider is merely an exhibitor, NO.

54. The National, in New York.

55. The American Royal, in Kansas City, Missouri.

56. The Los Angeles National Spring Show.

57. The Kentucky State Fair, in Louisville.

58. The Royal Winter Fair, in Toronto.

59. The International, Olympia, London.

60. The Royal Dublin Society Horse Show.

61. A cross-country ride over obstacles against time; the form of the rider, equitation, and the performance of the horse are given consideration in the scoring.

62. (a) The Three-Day Event (All-around equestrian competition)—Teams of three and individual, consisting of three phases:
    (1) A test of training (dressage);
    (2) An endurance test—consisting of a road test, cross-country, and steeplechase performance;
    (3) A jumping test.
    (b) The Individual Dressage Competition—Teams of three and individual.
    (c) The Prix des Nations (Jumping Competition)—Teams of three and individual.
    Each event is open to three riders and three horses from each competing nation.

63. Yes. In 1932 and again in 1948, the United States won the three-day team event.

64. The National Horse Show Saddle Seat Event, the American Horse Shows Association Saddle Seat Medal Class (no jumping), the A.S.P.C.A. Horsemanship Class (Maclay

Trophy), and the American Horse Shows Association Hunter Seat Medal Class.

65. Those who have not reached their eighteenth birthday, according to A.H.S.A. rules.

66. By increasing the distance between the bars, spreading and broadening the obstacle, as well as increasing the height.

67. The rules of the Federation Equestre Internationale "F.E.I."

68. Blue, 5 points; Red, 3 points; Yellow, 2 points; White, 1 point.

69. Fourteen—Argentina, Brazil, Canada, Chile, Cuba, France, Great Britain, Ireland, Italy, Mexico, Peru, Spain, Venezuela, and West Germany.

70. Yes. In 1931 and 1932 the United States Army Team won, and in 1957, 1959, 1960, and 1962, the United States Equestrian Team, made up of civilian riders, won.

71. The American Horse Shows Association.

72. One at which total cash prizes do not exceed $500, except 100 per cent. sweepstakes, and which is limited to 4 sessions, 48 hours and 60 classes.

73. Right-handed; i.e. the center of the ring is on the rider's right.

74. A Gig.

75. Four. Registered, Recorded, Guest, and Special.

76. One who has judged and been officially designated a judge at two or more shows in a given Division—applies to men and women 21 years of age or older, amateur and professional.

77. One who has been officially designated as a Recorded Judge

to obtain experience. Also applies to men and women 21 or over, amateur and professional.

78. Twenty-one.

79. They are: Arabian, Appaloosa, Combined Training, Dressage, Harness Pony, Hackney, Hunter, Jumper, Morgan, Palomino, Parade, Pinto, Roadster, Saddle, Shetland, Walking, Welsh, Western Hunter, Saddle and Stock Seat Equitation.

80. Have them change horses and have them perform similar tests on their new mounts.

Fox Hunting

AVERAGE SCORES:
(Per cent answered correctly)

5 who do not ride	11
5 who ride but do not hunt	29
5 who hunt but not members of hunt staffs	65
5 amateur members of hunt staffs	87
3 Masters of Foxhounds	94

To determine your score (or anyone else's), count the number of questions answered correctly and consult the table on pages 225 and 226.

The answers to the questions in this section will be found following the list of questions, on pages 112 through 118.

FOX HUNTING
QUESTIONS

1. What is the male fox called?

2. What is the female fox called?

3. What are young foxes called?

4. Name two of the nicknames commonly used in referring to the fox.

5. What type or breed of fox is most generally found in the northeastern part of the United States?

6. What type or breed of fox is most generally found in the states south of Virginia?

7. What type or breed of fox is most generally found in the near and middle west?

8. What type or breed of fox is most generally found in England?

9. What is the fox's mask?

10. What is the fox's brush?

11. What is the fox's pad?

12. What is the cluster of white hairs at the end of a fox's tail called?

13. What is a covert?

14. What is the fox's abode called?

15. What is meant by "stopping the earth"?

16. What is meant by a "straight necked" fox?

17. What is meant by a "breast high scent"?

18. What is meant by "cubbing"?

19. What is the correct manner of referring to the number of hounds in a hunting pack?

20. How would you refer to 15 hounds?

21. Where is a hound generally marked to show his breeding and ownership?

22. What is a hound's dewlap?

23. What are a hound's hackles?

24. What type or breed of foxhound is hunted by the majority of recognized Hunts in the United States?

25. What other types or breeds of foxhounds are generally hunted in the United States?

26. In what way does the American foxhound differ chiefly from the English foxhound?

27. What is meant by to "give tongue"?

28. What other terms have a similar meaning?

29. What is a dog pack?

30. What is meant by the "young entry"?

31. What is meant by "blooding" hounds?

32. What is meant by "roading" hounds?

33. What is meant by "walking" hounds?

34. What are "couplings"?

35. What, other than conformation, are the chief characteristics of a good hunter (horse)?

36. Is the hunter a distinct breed?

37. Of which recognized breed does the hunter contain the greatest infusion of blood?

38. Why are hunters' legs not clipped?

39. What does a red ribbon on a horse's tail indicate?

40. What is a hunting breast-plate?

41. Where is the sandwich case carried?

42. Where is the flask carried?

43. Name two places the horn may be carried.

44. How does one greet the Master at a formal meet?

45. Hounds approach or are about to pass you, you are mounted and off the road; what should you do?

46. What is the correct way of warning others of the approach or proximity of hounds?

47. If there is occasion to lower more than one fence rail, which is lowered first?

48. Who are the hunt staff?

49. Who carries a horn?

50. What is meant by "the Master carries the horn"?

51. Approximately how many recognized and registered hunts are there in the United States?

52. What is the name of the governing body of foxhunting in the United States?

53. What is "the field"?

54. Name two of the conditions in general most favorable to good scent.

55. What is a cast?

56. What is a check?

57. What is meant by "drawing" a covert?

58. What is meant by "holding up" cubs?

59. What do you do when you view a fox leave covert—when you are in sight of the Master or Huntsman?

60. What do you do when you view a fox leave covert—when you are not in sight of the Master or Huntsman?

61. What are the usual positions of the various members of the hunt staff when they take their hounds to and from a meet?

62. When drawing a covert, what are the positions of the various members of the hunt staff?

63. To what does the term "ratcatcher" refer?

64. Who traditionally wear black velvet hunting caps?

65. Which way should the ribbons of the bow on the back of the cap be placed?

66. What is the difference in the way a professional and an amateur whip carries the leather?

67. What is the origin of the scarlet hunting coat?

68. What is the derivation of the term "pink" applied to hunting attire?

69. Which color, in addition to that of the hunt uniform, is considered correct for formal hunting attire?

70. Is any color other than scarlet correctly used as the basic color of a hunt uniform?

71. What should be the color of the boot garter?

72. What is a "drag" hunt?

73. What is a "drag line"?

74. In which country is stag hunting most prevalent?

75. What are the classifications of hunted stag?

76. Whose is the direct responsibility for the conduct and dress of the field?

77. To what does "pigsticking" refer?

78. If hounds come upon you from the rear, what do you do?

79. Name a great fictional fox hunting character who freely dispensed good advice in cockney.

80. Name a famous old English hunting song.

FOX HUNTING

ANSWERS

1. A dog fox.

2. A vixen.

3. Cubs.

4. Reynard; Charlie; Charles James; Uncle Remus.

5. The red fox.

6. The grey fox.

7. The red fox.

8. The red fox.

9. His head.

10. His tail.

11. His foot.

12. The chape (pronounced chap). Sometimes also called the feathers.

13. A small wood, thicket, underbrush or other similar place, where foxes are sheltered and are apt to be found.

14. His den.

15. Closing or blocking the entrance to a hole, into which a fox may go to "ground" (or "earth").

16. A fox which runs in a straight line for a long distance without resorting to trickery to throw the hounds off his line.

17. A scent that is particularly good (strong).

18. Training young hounds to hunt the fox, pick up scent, travel together, obey and become used to the work and routine of hunting; also, in some instances, to "blood" young hounds and to scatter the fox cubs. In the United States often confined in its meaning to early pre-season hunting.

19. As so many couple.

20. Seven and a half couple.

21. On the ears.

22. The pendulous fold of skin under the hound's neck.

23. The long hairs on the back of his neck.

24. The American.

25. English and Cross Bred largely; and to some extent Welsh.

26. Characteristically the American hound has a greater cry than the English hound and uses it more freely when on the line (a great advantage in the American hilly, wooded country); he has a better nose, is more persistent in hunting (most essential in the dry climate frequent in America); he is lighter and smaller (hence more adapted to the rough American country); his "hare" foot is more adaptable to the rough going in America than the "cat" foot of the English hound.

27. Refers to the sound or bay ("cry") hounds make when working on the scent of a fox or other quarry.

28. To give voice; to speak; to cry; answer to or honor the line; —as a noun, music.

29. A pack of hounds, all of which are males.

30. The youngest (newest) hounds of a pack of fox hounds.

31. Encouraging them to break up their fox after they have

caught him so that they will be more keen for the chase. (More common in England than in the United States.)

32. Exercising hounds by taking them along a road or cross-country, at slow gaits, the hunt staff being mounted or walking.

33. Turning over young hounds to members or farmers, a few to each, who will take care of and exercise them until they are ready to be trained for and used for hunting.

34. Also called "couples." A device, consisting of two links with a ring at each end, which is attached to the collars of each of two hounds by straps to couple them so that they must work together, usually a younger with an older hound.

35. Ability, reliability, and sure-footedness in jumping obstacles; endurance and staying power; good manners, especially with hounds; a good way of going; uniformity of pace.

36. No.

37. The Thoroughbred.

38. To afford protection against underbrush, thickets, thorns, etc., and, as a horse does not sweat through the skin of his legs, there is no necessity for clipping them.

39. That the horse is a kicker; beware of him and keep at a distance.

40. A leather strap encircling his neck and resting on his chest, or a strap about his chest supported by smaller straps near the withers, attached to the saddle and the girth to prevent the saddle slipping to the rear.

41. Off side, close to the cantle.

42. Near side, close to the pommel.

43. (a) Between the first and second button of the hunting coat; (b) In a leather case on the saddle, off (or near) side close to the pommel.

44. By raising one's hat and, if one desires, greeting him with "Good Morning, Sir," or some similar salutation.

45. Face your horse's head toward them.

46. By saying: " 'Ware hounds." (The staff says "Hounds please.")

47. The lower or bottom rail.

48. The Master of Fox Hounds; the Huntsman; the Whippers-in ("Whips")—at least two; and in some instances, a Field Master.

49. The Master (optional) and the Huntsman (always).

50. That the Master hunts his hounds, rather than employing a professional Huntsman.

51. 110 in 1964.

52. The Masters of Foxhounds Association of America.

53. Members of the Hunt and their guests, other than, and as distinguished from, the staff.

54. When the barometer is steady or a little on the high side; when it is slightly damp; when there is a gentle, steady wind and the fox runs up-wind; when frost is coming in; in grass land, as opposed to plowed land.

55. A specific manner of spreading hounds in search of the scent, usually when it has been lost. Generally hounds are cast by the Huntsman, but frequently they cast themselves in search of the fox's "line."

56. An interruption in the run (chase), caused by hounds losing the scent.

57. To lead (direct or urge) hounds into a covert in search of a fox.

58. During the cubbing season, surrounding a covert with the staff and the field to prevent cubs running out; that is, if they attempt to come out, driving them back in, to assure the young hounds of a find and a kill. Foxes or cubs that do go away are not run. More prevalent in England than in the United States.

59. Hold your hat at arm's length above your head at the spot where you last saw the fox, turn your horse's head in the direction he went away, and utter not a word.

60. Shout, "Tally-ho."

61. The Master, the First Whipper-in followed by the Huntsman with the hounds, the Second Whipper-in bringing up the rear. If, however, the Master is not an active member of the hunt staff, he follows the staff.

62. The Huntsman (or the Master, if he hunts his hounds) is with his hounds in the covert near its center. The Whippers-in are on either side of him near the edge of the covert so that they may view the fox away. The Master, if he does not hunt his hounds, is outside the covert holding up the field.

63. Informal riding attire, as opposed to formal hunting attire; a tweed coat, soft felt hat, brown boots, etc.

64. Only members of a hunt staff, hunt secretaries, ex-masters and children, at the discretion of the master.

65. Up, if the wearer is an amateur; down, if a professional. (This convention is not, however, strictly adhered to.)

66. The amateur, inside his coat; the professional, outside his coat. (Frequently in America, however, Whippers-in do not carry a leather.)

67. There are several and various theories. The one most generally accepted by hunting men and those who have made a study of the subject is that scarlet was used by the early fox hunters to distinguish themselves from the harriers and stag hunters, who traditionally wore green, and sometimes blue or gray. Scarlet was probably popular because of the predominance of this color in the English military uniform. Also, Henry II decreed fox hunting a royal sport and that members of the Hunt should wear the royal livery —scarlet. Previous to the ascendancy of fox hunting, the hunt uniforms were, as a rule, tailored in the colors of the Master's livery.

68. The popularity of a fashionable gentlemen's tailor, by the name of Pink, famous for his fine sporting turnouts early in the nineteenth century. (Although the term "pink" might have been used previously as slang for scarlet, there appears in writing at the time to be little use of it prior to the advent of Pink, the tailor. In any event he seems to have emphasized and popularized the term.)

69. Black.

70. Yes. While scarlet is most general and has come to be traditionally associated with fox hunting, any color is correct and many hunt uniforms are of other colors, such as blue, gray, yellow etc., some of them, especially in England, corresponding to the livery of an early or the present master.

71. If white breeches are worn, white or nearly white (buff), the same as the color of the breeches; with brown breeches, it is brown. Women wear black patent leather boot garters.

72. A "hunt" or chase in which the pack follows an artificial scent (aniseed or fox litter) usually laid by hand, using strips of impregnated cloth or, less frequently, by dragging it in a cloth sack behind a horse; as opposed to hunting a fox.

73. A planned and maintained route across country, containing a succession of known fences, along which the "dragged" scent is laid.

74. France.

75. Free (wild) and carted.

76. The Field Master.

77. Hunting the wild boar with a lance, without hounds. (Characteristically, in India.)

78. Say "Ware hounds" (for beware).

79. John Jorrock, Esq., a mythical character created by Robert Smith Surtees.

80. "John Peel" by John Woodcock Graves.

Flat Racing

AVERAGE SCORES:

(Per cent answered correctly)

5 who ride but have not witnessed a flat race at a recognized track.   16

5 who do not ride or own horses, but have witnessed at least three races at a recognized track.   34

5 who ride or own horses and have witnessed at least three races at a recognized track.   52

3 jockeys   89

3 racing officials   94

To determine your score (or any one else's), count the number of questions answered correctly and consult the table on pages 225 and 226.

The answers to the question in this section will be found following the list of questions, on pages 126 through 132.

FLAT RACING
QUESTIONS

1. Tell within two seconds the running record for a mile in the United States.

2. In what year was it established?

3. By what horse?

4. Where?

5. In which State are the greatest number of Thoroughbreds produced (foaled)?

6. Which State has the greatest number of tracks (mile or more) in regular use?

7. What locality in the United States is generally considered the best for breeding race horses?

8. Which well-known jockey originated the forward racing seat?

9. What is meant by a "Garrison Finish"?

10. Name the trainer who has saddled the greatest number of winners.

11. Who is Earl Sande?

12. Which State pioneered horse racing in the United States?

13. What is the oldest stakes race in the United States?

14. At what distance do 2-year-olds usually race (in the summer and early fall)?

15. What is good time for this distance?

16. At what distance are the most important 3-year-old races run?

17. What is good time for this distance?

18. At what distance are the most important races for horses four years old and older run?

19. In which year and where was the Washington, D.C., International Invitation—1½ miles in the turf—inaugurated?

20. What is the distance of a furlong in yards?

21. In which direction are races run in the United States?

22. In England?

23. In or near what city is the HIALEAH track?

24. In or near what city is BAY MEADOWS?

25. In or near what city is ARLINGTON PARK?

26. In or near what city is the FAIR GROUNDS?

27. Where is the KENTUCKY DERBY run?

28. Where is the PREAKNESS Stakes run?

29. Where is the HOPEFUL Stakes run?

30. Where is the AMERICAN DERBY run?

31. What races are included in the "Triple Crown"?

32. Which races are generally considered the "Triple Crown" of the handicap division (horses three years old and older)?

33. What is generally considered the most important stakes race in the West (United States)?

34. Name two of what are generally considered the most important races for 2-year-olds in the United States.

35. What is generally considered the most important race for 3-year-olds in the United States?

36. What is generally considered the most important race for 3-year-olds and *up* in the United States?

37. What is a "Produce" race?

38. What is the chief difference between the race tracks in England and the United States?

39. What race in the United States most nearly corresponds to the English Derby at Epsom Downs?

40. What is the governing body of Thoroughbred racing in the United States?

41. What is a Thoroughbred?

42. What are the basic requirements for admission to the Thoroughbred stud book?

43. What was the record for a mile in 1800?

44. What was the record for a mile in 1850?

45. What was the record for a mile in 1900?

46. How many fillies have won the Kentucky Derby?

47. What is a "Boat Race"?

48. What is a "Claiming Race"?

49. What is meant by "breezed under wraps"?

50. What is meant by "rating"?

51. What is meant by "5,000 added"?

52. What, essentially, is the pari-mutuel system or plan of betting?

53. What is a "daily double"?

54. What is meant by "odds on"?

55. What is meant by "to show"?

56. What is meant by "to place"?

57. How is the age of a horse determined under the Rules of Racing?

58. Approximately what does a racing saddle weigh?

59. What, approximately, is the usual weight of a jockey, less his equipment?

60. What is the World's record for a running mile?

61. Name the greatest money winning race horse (of all time).

62. Name the greatest money winning sire (of all time).

63. How many horses have won the Triple Crown?

64. How often has the same horse won the Futurity and the Kentucky Derby?

65. Which horse was known as "THE MILE KING"?

66. Which as "OLD BONES"?

67. Which as "BIG RED"?

68. What is unique about the record of KINCSEM?

69. Who was PHAR LAP?

70. What is the difference between a "stake" and a "sweepstake"?

71. What is the distance run in the Kentucky Derby?

72. What is the distance run in the Preakness?

73. Where is the oldest race course in the United States still in use?

74. By what means are horses starting in a race handicapped?

75. Name two conditions for which horses are handicapped.

76. What code of rules governs the conduct of American flat racing?

77. With whom are racing colors registered?

78. What is a "chute" as applied to race tracks?

79. In how many races was Man o' War defeated?

80. What is usually considered the most effective barometer of the state of the Thoroughbred racing industry in the United States?

FLAT RACING

ANSWERS

1. 1 minute, 33 1/5 seconds.

2. In 1956 (June 9) and equalled in 1959 (June 27).

3. Swaps, as a 4-year-old, carrying 128 pounds; and Intentionally, as a 3-year-old, carrying 121 pounds.

4. Swaps, at Hollywood Park, California; Intentionally, at Washington Park, Illinois.

5. Kentucky. Next, in order, are: California, Virginia, Illinois, Florida, Texas, and Maryland.

6. California with six. New York and Illinois each have four.

7. The blue grass country of Kentucky in the vicinity of Lexington.

8. Tod Sloan.

9. A horse coming from behind with a whirlwind burst of speed during the run through the stretch (finish). Derived from "Snapper" Garrison's characteristic manner of riding his races.

10. HIRSCH JACOBS. He has led the field eleven times.

11. A well-known jockey of the 1920's. He rode Gallant Fox to 9 victories out of 10 starts for a record breaking year's earnings. Since his retirement from the saddle, he has been a prominent trainer.

12. New York. On the Hempstead plains of Long Island in the 1660's.

13. The Travers originated in 1864 at Saratoga.

14. Five and six furlongs.

15. 1 minute and 11 or 12 seconds for six furlongs.

16. 1⅛ to 1½ miles.

17. 1 minute, 50 seconds for 1⅛ mile. 2 minutes, 30 seconds for 1½. 2 minutes, 3 seconds for 1¼ miles.

18. 1¼ miles, but, more generally, 1 to 2 miles.

19. In 1952, at the Laurel race course, Maryland.

20. 220 yards.

21. Counterclockwise.

22. Both clockwise and counterclockwise—but more generally the former.

23. Near Miami, Florida.

24. San Mateo (near San Francisco), California.

25. Near Chicago, Illinois.

26. New Orleans, Louisiana.

27. Churchill Downs (near Louisville), Kentucky.

28. Pimlico, Maryland.

29. Saratoga, New York.

30. Washington Park (near Chicago), Illinois.

31. The Kentucky Derby, Preakness, and Belmont Stakes—all for 3-year-olds.

32. The Brooklyn Handicap, at 1¼ miles; the Metropolitan

Handicap, at 1 mile; and the Suburban Handicap, at 1¼ miles.

33. The Santa Anita Handicap run at Arcadia, California.

34. The Futurity and the Champagne Stakes at Aqueduct, N.Y.; the Arlington Futurity at Arlington Park, Ill.; the Hopeful Stakes at Saratoga, N.Y.; and the Garden State at Garden State Park, N.J.

35. The Kentucky Derby at Churchill Downs, Kentucky. (Although some will say the Preakness, Belmont Stakes, Arlington Classic, Travers or American Derby.)

36. The Suburban Handicap at Aqueduct, New York. (Some may say the Santa Anita Handicap at Arcadia, California.)

37. One in which the get of specified sires only are eligible— a race for the unborn produce of horses named at the time nominations for the event close.

38. In the United States (for flat racing) they are almost invariably cinder or natural earth; in England the footing is generally grass turf.

39. The Belmont Stakes at Aqueduct, New York. Both are for 3-year-olds; the Belmont distance is 1½ miles; the Epsom Derby, 1 mile, 881 yards.

40. The individual state racing commissions within their respective states. The National Association of State Racing Commissions, a voluntary organization acts in an *advisory* capacity.

41. A specific breed of running horse registered in the "American Stud Book" or its foreign equivalent. The name Thoroughbred should not be confused with the term "purebred."

42. Direct descent, in all branches of its pedigree from one or more of the three foundation sires: The Darley Arabian, the Gololphin Arabian and the Byerly Turk.

43. 1:55—although it is somewhat obscure as most races at that time were at 2, 3 or 4 miles.

44. 1:45½ by Flying Dutchman.

45. 1:35½ by Salvator.

46. Only one—Regret in 1915.

47. A crooked or "fixed" race.

48. A race in which any of the horses running may be bought (claimed) by anyone, except the owner for the price posted by the owner prior to the race.

49. The rider holding a horse well in hand at a pace slower than he can and would gallop if he were not restrained by his rider.

50. To steady a horse, hold him back a little up to the final dash of a race at an even rate of speed so that he will have something left for a strong finish.

51. That the sum subscribed by the entries in a stake or sweep-stakes has been increased by a $5,000 additional contribu-tion—usually by the racing association.

52. A system of pooling all bets and distributing the total, less a percentage commission (usually 10%), proportionately among the holders of tickets on the winning, second and third horses. The odds therefore depend on the number placing bets (holding tickets) on the winning horse. The plan is distinguished from individual bookmaking in which the bookmaker establishes the odds and his percentages.

53. A bet placed on a horse in each of the first two races, which, if the horse bet in the first race wins, is automatically placed on the horse bet in the second race—thus materially increasing the winnings if the horse selected in the second race also wins. If *both* horses do not win, the bet is lost.

54. A wager which, if won, will return a sum less than that bet. For example, 1 to 2. You wager $200 to win $100, collecting, if you win, $300—the $200 you put up and $100 winnings.

55. To come in THIRD in a race.

56. To come in SECOND in a race.

57. By reckoning from January 1 of the year in which it was foaled.

58. 1½ to 2 pounds.

59. 90 to 110 pounds.

60. 1:32 by MOPSUS on June 22, 1939 at Brighton, England. (The Brighton track is a straightaway, slightly downhill.)

61. Through 1963 it is ROUND TABLE, owned by Travis M. Kerr, with just short of $1,750,000. However, KELSO, who is still racing, and is owned by Mrs. Richard C. duPont, has already won a little over $1,580,000. (Three other horses have earned over a million dollars: NASHUA, $1,288,565; CARRY BACK, $1,241,165; and CITATION, $1,085,760.)

62. NASRULLAH, imported, whose get have earned over $11½ (exactly $11,580,122) through 1963. The get of BULL LEA, owned by Calumet Farm, have earned about $9½ million ($9,497,260).

63. Eight. SIR BARTON in 1919; GALLANT FOX in 1930; OMAHA in 1935; WAR ADMIRAL in 1937; WHIRLA-WAY in 1941; COUNT FLEET in 1943; ASSAULT in 1946; and CITATION in 1948.

64. Only once, by CITATION in 1947 and 1948.

65. ROAMER.

66. EXTERMINATOR.

67. MAN O' WAR.

68. She had the longest string of victories known to the turf, winning 54 consecutive races. (Her career ended in 1880).

69. A famous Australian gelding, winner of the Melbourne Cup, who as a five-year-old in 1932 arrived in the United States to race against leading American horses, including TWENTY GRAND. He died shortly after a warm up race on the West Coast.

70. In a stakes race the entry fees are usually divided among the winner, second and third; in a sweepstakes, the winner takes all. But often "stakes" is merely a corruption of "sweepstakes."

71. 1¼ miles.

72. 1³⁄₁₆ miles.

73. Saratoga, New York. It was inaugurated in 1864.

74. By carrying additional weight.

75. Age, sex, performance (amount and number of previous winnings) and novice (apprentice) rider.

76. The Jockey Club's Rules of Racing

77. The Jockey Club (in New York and Delaware) or the State racing commission.

78. A short straightaway course or strip, usually 3 to 6 furlongs in length—frequently a straightened extension of a turn on the back stretch on which races of a short distance may be run without starting on a turn.

79. Only one—out of 21 starts.

80. The annual yearling sales at Saratoga, New York and the Keeneland sales at Lexington, Kentucky.

Steeplechasing

P.B.

AVERAGE SCORES:

(Per cent answered correctly)

5 who ride but have not witnessed a steeplechase or hunt race meeting.   10

5 who do not ride or own horses but have witnessed at least three steeplechases or hunt race meetings.   27

5 who ride and own horses and have witnessed at least three steeplechases or hunt race meetings.   49

3 amateur steeplechase riders.   92

3 members of hunts racing committees.   92

To determine your score (or anyone else's), count the number of questions answered correctly and consult the table on pages 225 and 226.

The answers to the questions in this section will be found following the list of questions, on pages 140 through 146.

STEEPLECHASING

QUESTIONS

1. What is a Steeplechase?
2. What is a Point-to-Point?
3. What is a Hunt Race Meeting?
4. Name three types of obstacles used in jumping races.
5. What is the usual distance of a steeplechase run at a race course?
6. What is the usual distance of a steeplechase at a hunt race meeting?
7. What is the chief difference between the seat used in flat racing and in steeplechasing?
8. What protective device must be worn by a rider in a steeplechase?
9. At what weight do amateur steeplechase jockeys usually ride in hunt races?
10. Is there any prohibition with respect to a horse carrying *over* weight?
11. What is the name of the governing body of steeplechasing in the United States?
12. Why were some riders referred to as "Mr." and others not?
13. Name a well-known American amateur steeplechase rider of the 1930's who rode in the English Grand National and who is also a high goal polo player?

14. What rule is there with respect to the minimum age a horse is permitted to run in a steeplechase?

15. What is the height of the *usual* timber obstacle in the United States?

16. What are the minimum requirements for (dimensions of) a water jump?

17. What generally is the height of the larger brush fences in the United States?

18. What, approximately, is the LENGTH of a racing horse's leap over the average obstacle?

19. For what purpose are red flags displayed on race obstacles?

20. What is the distinction between a red and a blue flag on the course?

21. What is the purpose of white flags displayed on obstacles?

22. Which race course in the world has the highest BRUSH obstacles?

23. Which race course in the world has the highest TIMBER obstacles?

24. What is the minimum weight permitted in races exclusively for hunters?

25. What is the minimum weight permitted in any Steeplechase?

26. What is a Hurdle race?

27. Which State produces the greatest number of steeplechasing horses?

28. Which State has the greatest number of jumping races—of all kinds?

29. What limitation is there with respect to the distance of a steeplechase for *hunters?*

30. What, approximately, is the range in age of steeplechase horses in top competition?

31. In about what time will a good 'chaser cover a TWO MILE course?

32. In about what time will a good 'chaser cover a FOUR MILE course?

33. Are steeplechase horses usually handicapped?

34. In general, have steeplechasers had flat racing experience?

35. Have horses unsuccessful as 'chasers had any success on the flat?

36. What is the chief difference between the obstacles in Steeplechases in the United States and in England?

37. Tell, within five years, when the first English Grand National was run.

38. Where is the Grand National steeplechase run in England?

39. What is the length of the course?

40. How many jumps are there?

41. What is the fastest time recorded for the race?

42. How many riders have been fatally injured?

43. How many American BRED horses have won the race?

44. How many American OWNED horses have won the race?

45. What is the top weight carried in the Aintree Grand National?

46. What is the age limit for horses running in the Aintree Grand National?

47. Among the winners of the Aintree Grand National have the greatest number been stallions, geldings or mares?

48. Where is the Grand National Steeplechase run in the United States?

49. In what important respect does the Grand National Steeplechase course in the U. S. differ from that in England?

50. When was the Grand National Steeplechase in the U. S. first run?

51. What is distinctive of the Grand National Point-to-Point run at Hereford, Maryland?

52. Are there now (1964) more or less brush courses than there were in 1900?

53. What award does the winner of the Maryland Hunt Cup receive?

54. In what year was the race inaugurated?

55. Has any horse won it three times since 1930?

56. How many riders in this race have been fatally injured?

57. Where has the race been run since 1930?

58. Over what distance?

59. State within thirty seconds the fastest recorded time for the race?

60. What is the origin of the term "steeplechase"?

61. In approximately what year did the first jumping race on a regular track in the United States take place?

62. Which steeplechase in the United States has the greatest money value?

63. What is the width of the usual brush obstacle?

64. What is meant by "catch weights"?

65. What is a "Liverpool"?

66. Is the steeplechase horse a distinct breed?

67. In general what breed is the steeplechase horse?

68. From what country do most of the imported horses come?

69. If a rider is dismounted, may he remount and continue the race?

70. If a rider falls and his horse gets away, is caught by a spectator and returned to him, may he continue the race?

71. If a rail on an obstacle is broken, may other horses jump the broken panel?

72. If a horse runs out at an obstacle or gets off the course, under what conditions may he continue the race?

73. What is a "Walk-Over"?

74. What is done if a rider weighs in three pounds *overweight* after a race?

75. What is done if a rider weighs in three pounds *light* after a race?

76. Under what conditions may a horse finish a race with a rider other than the one up at the start?

77. What is the longest steeplechase in the United States?

78. What is generally the minimum distance for steeplechases over timber?

79. How many fences are required per mile?

80. Where a money prize is provided for second place, under what condition may a horse who finishes second *not* be placed (i.e. not receive second money)?

STEEPLECHASING
ANSWERS

1. A horse race over brush obstacles on a prescribed course. The term is sometimes used broadly to mean any kind of horse race over obstacles, of whatever nature, on a course or cross country.
2. A race across natural country and natural fences from one specified point to another (and sometimes return) over any route the rider chooses.
3. A series of races over a course in the country, held under the auspices of a Hunt or a hunting group.
4. Timber (post and rail), brush and hurdles.
5. 2 to 2½ miles.
6. 2 to 4 miles.
7. The usual seat adopted for flat racing is characterized by an abnormally short stirrup permitting a position well forward over the horse's withers. See sketch below.

Steeplechase riders adopt a somewhat more normal seat, the stirrup leathers are longer and the rider is more in the saddle. See sketch below.

8. A light but strong fiber skull cap, under the silk.

9. Up to 170 pounds and quite generally 150-160.

10. Yes; except when an amateur rider is up, a horse may not carry more than 5 pounds overweight.

11. The National Steeplechase and Hunt Association.

12. All riders other than professionals were referred to as "Mr."

13. George H. ("Pete") Bostwick, of Westbury, Long Island, New York.

14. He may not run until August 1st of the year in which he is three years old.

15. From 4 to 5 feet.

16. 12 feet wide and 2 feet deep with a fence not less than 2 feet high on the take off side.

17. 5 to 6 feet.

18. Approximately 20 feet.

19. To indicate the *inside* of the course and thus the direction in which the obstacles are to be taken. The flag should be on the rider's left.

20. None. Either a red or a blue flag indicates that the obstacles should be jumped with that flag on the rider's left.

21. They indicate the *outside* of the course, the rider jumping the obstacle so as to leave it on his right.

22. William duPont's Foxcatcher Farm course at Fair Hill, Maryland, and the course at Auteuil, France. The larger obstacles average 6 feet.

23. The Maryland Hunt Cup course. The fences average about 4 feet 3 inches, the biggest are 4 feet, 10 and 8 inches.

24. 145 pounds.

25. 130 pounds.

26. A jumping race in which the obstacles are "sheep hurdles" —panels of light wood fencing with brush set in it and inclined at an angle of about 60 degrees from the ground. They look like this:

27. Kentucky. Virginia is second, Maryland third.

28. New York. New Jersey is second, Virginia third. If the question were confined to Hunt racing, excluding chases at the big tracks, the order would be: Virginia, Pennsylvania, New Jersey.

29. A minimum of 2½ miles over brush and 3½ miles over timber.

30. 4 to 10.

31. About 3 minutes, 50 seconds.

32. About 8½ minutes.

33. Yes—usually for age, sex, apprentice or inexperienced riders and for past performance.

34. Yes, many have run on the flat as two- or three-year-olds.

35. As a rule, no—with few exceptions. Azucar, which won the first running of the Santa Anita Handicap, is one.

36. In the United States there are a number of timber as well as brush courses and races—in England the obstacles are almost entirely brush. Hurdle racing is growing in popularity in both countries.

37. It was inaugurated in 1839.

38. At Aintree, near Liverpool.

39. About 4½ miles—exactly, 4 miles, 856 yards.

40. 30.

41. 9 minutes, 20 seconds, by GOLDEN MILLER in 1934.

42. Only one, James Wynne, in 1862.

43. Two: RUBIO, owned by an Englishman, in 1908, and BATTLESHIP, owned by Mrs. Scott, in 1938.

44. Four: SERGEANT MURPHY, owned by Stephen Sanford, in 1923, JACK HORNER, owned by A. C. Schwartz, in 1926; KELLSBORO JACK, owned by Mrs. F. Ambrose Clark, in 1933 and BATTLESHIP in 1938.

45. 172 pounds.

46. They must be 6 years old or more.

47. Geldings, predominantly.

48. At Belmont Park, N. Y.

49. Chiefly in that the American course is only 3 miles in length, and it is less difficult to negotiate.

50. In 1899.

51. It is over timber.

52. More.

53. A silver cup—no purse.

54. In 1894.

55. Yes, three: BLOCKADE in 1938, 1939, and 1940; WINTON in 1942, 1946, and 1947; and PINE PEP in 1949, 1950, and 1952.

56. None.

57. In the Worthington Valley at Glyndon, near Baltimore.

58. About 4 miles.

59. The record is 8 minutes, 43⅘ seconds, established by FLUC-TUATE in 1960. Previous record was 8 minutes, 44 seconds, by BLOCKADE in 1938.

60. In the 17th century it was usual for the sporting gentry to race cross-country from a designated point a distance of approximately four miles to "Yon church steeple"—the only reference point clearly visible on the horizon. Hence such

a race was termed a STEEPLECHASE. These point to point races, if the desirable shortest course were followed, naturally required jumping fences. Ultimately, the majority of races over fences were confined to smaller areas, prescribed courses and more or less standard obstacles—with a church steeple no longer required for reference. The name, however, stuck.

61. In 1834, at the Jockey Club track in Washington, D. C.

62. The Temple Gwathmey Steeplechase at Belmont Park. Its top value was $39,225 to the winner in 1955.

63. About 3 to 3½ feet.

64. Refers to a race run without regard to weight carried.

65. An obstacle composed of an open ditch in front of a high brush fence, generally with a low rail on the take off side. It looks like this:

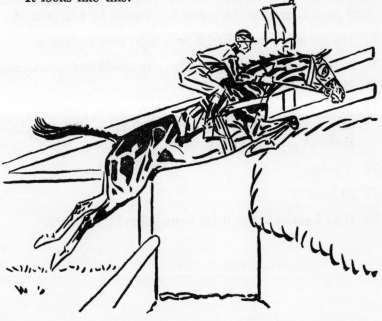

66. No.

67. Usually it is a Thoroughbred.

68. England and Ireland.

69. Yes—provided he does so in the space between the obstacle he last jumped and the next jump, or the last fence and the finish.

70. Yes—provided he remounts in the area described in the preceding answer.

71. Yes—and usually they do.

72. If he turns back and continues the race from that point.

73. A situation where only one horse (or several horses belonging to a single interest) is ready to start a race at the appointed time.

74. The *rider* is fined, suspended or ruled off if he is more than 2 pounds overweight, *unless* it is caused by rain or mud.

75. His *horse* is disqualified if he is light over 2 pounds.

76. It is *not* permitted now under any conditions; some years ago it was.

77. There is none recorded longer than "about 4 miles." There are several timber races at this distance, the Maryland Hunt Cup being one of them.

78. 3 miles.

79. At least 6.

80. If he finishes 5 minutes or more behind the winner.

Harness Racing

AVERAGE SCORES:
(Per cent answered correctly)

5 who ride but have not witnessed a harness race.	12
5 who do not ride or own horses, but have witnessed at least three harness race meetings.	26
5 who ride or own horses and have witnessed at least 3 harness race meetings.	54
3 drivers.	96
3 owners.	86

To determine your score (or anyone else's), count the number of questions answered correctly and consult the table on pages 225 and 226.

The answers to the questions in this section will be found following the list of questions, on pages 154 through 162.

HARNESS RACING

QUESTIONS

1. Which horse is generally agreed to have provided the foundation stock for the trotter?

2. What is the official designation of the breed of trotters and pacers?

3. What is the difference between the trot and the pace?

4. Which is the faster gait—the trot or the pace?

5. Were trotters ever raced under saddle?

6. What is the name of the vehicle used in harness racing?

7. What is meant by a 2:05 Bar Trot?

8. Approximately what is the age range of harness horses when they establish their best records?

9. What, approximately, is the length of a good trotter's stride?

10. What is the governing body of harness racing?

11. What is "The Grand Circuit"?

12. What are the conditions for inclusion of a horse in the Trotting Register?

13. What were these conditions (12) originally?

14. What vehicle other than the sulky was used in harness racing?

15. Which State produces the greatest number of harness horses?

16. In which State are the greatest number of harness racing tracks in regular use?

17. Which state has the greatest number of race meetings at pari-mutuel raceways?

18. In what countries other than the United States is harness racing most popular? Name three.

19. Which races are generally considered to constitute Trotting's Triple Crown?

20. What is generally considered the "Capital City" of harness racing?

21. What locality is generally known as the home (birthplace) of harness racing?

22. Do trotters race clockwise or counterclockwise?

23. What is a "classified" race?

24. What is a "free for all" race?

25. What is meant by a 2:10 class for trotters (or a 10 Trot)?

26. What recent change has been made in harness racing with respect to heats?

27. What is meant by "scoring"?

28. What is meant by "brushing"?

29. What is meant by "cheating"?

30. What is a "twice around"?

31. By how much has the trotting record for a mile been reduced in the last 25 years?

32. By how much has the pacing record for a mile been reduced in the last 25 years?

33. In about what year was the 2:40 or better mile trotting record established?

34. In about what year was the 2:30 or better mile trotting record established?

35. In about what year was the 2:20 or better mile trotting record established?

36. In about what year was the 2:10 or better mile trotting record established?

37. In what year was the 2 minute or better mile harness record established?

38. Name the horse and place.

39. In what year was the 2 minute or better mile trotted?

40. Name the horse and place.

41. What was considered a fast mile (top time classification) in 1870?

42. What was considered a fast mile (top time classification) in 1900?

43. What was considered a fast mile (top time classification) in 1920?

44. What is considered a fast mile (top time classification) to-day?

45. What is the record mile for trotters to-day?

46. What is the record mile for pacers to-day?

47. On the records, are harness geldings and stallions or mares the faster?

48. What important difference is there between the conditions under which the first horses to trot or pace a two minute

mile established their record and the conditions under which they are made to-day?

49. What is considered the most important race for 3-year-old trotters?

50. What is generally considered the most important harness racing fixture in the United States?

51. What is considered the most important race for 2-year-old trotters?

52. What is considered the most important race for 2-year-old pacers?

53. What is considered the most important race for 3-year-old pacers?

54. What is the oldest (longest established) fixed race for all age trotters?

55. As a rule, do trotters and pacers race each other?

56. What are the requirements for entry of a horse in the Hambletonian Stake?

57. What, approximately, is the record for 20 miles?

58. Approximately, what year was the first trotting race held on a regular track?

59. Approximately, how many horses have officially recorded a 2-minute or better trot?

60. Approximately, how many horses have officially recorded a 2-minute or better pace?

61. What recent improvement has been made in starting trotting and pacing races?

62. What is a "side wheeler"?

63. Name three slang terms used to describe pacers.

64. What are hopples?

65. Can a horse, whose natural gait is a pace, be trained to trot?

66. Name a device which will cause a natural pacer to trot.

67. What distinctive equipment is often found above a trotter's hoofs?

68. What, approximately, is the weight of a racing sulky?

69. Approximately when were bike wheels first used on racing sulkies?

70. What further major improvement in sulkies was made after the introduction of bike wheels?

71. Name three pieces of light harness equipment in addition to the reins and bit and not including the sulky.

72. Name three factors, other than the horse itself, which have an important bearing on a harness horse's racing speed?

73. In the '80s and early '90s, what did the letter K after a harness horse's record signify?

74. What is the greatest distance covered in harness races today?

75. Who was Bill Rysdyk?

76. What is remarkable about the record of Flora Temple?

77. What is remarkable about the record of Dan Patch?

78. What is remarkable about the record of Greyhound?

79. Name three famous Standardbred sires whose names are generally referred to in describing and grouping their descendants—progenitors of famous Standardbred blood lines? (Omit the foundation sire.)

80. What is the relationship, if any, between Hambletonian (Rysdyk's) and Messenger?

HARNESS RACING

1. Imported MESSENGER, a grey running horse stallion imported from England in 1788.

2. The American STANDARDBRED Horse.

3. In the TROT, the horse springs from one *diagonal* pair of legs to the other, i.e., the right fore and left hind, then the left fore and right hind. The action looks like this:

or this:

In the PACE, the horse springs from one *lateral* pair of legs to the other, i.e., the right fore and hind, then the left fore and hind. Like this:

or this:

4. The pace—but slightly.

5. Yes. The first trotting race was under saddle and trotters continued to be raced thus until approximately 1845. Trotting races under saddle are extensively indulged in and popular in France today.

6. A SULKY.

7. A trotting race limited to horses which have not won a race officially timed at 2 minutes and 5 seconds, or less.

8. 3 to 7 years old; some have been older, for example Flora Temple at 14!

9. 20 to 22 feet. Greyhound's stride was measured at 23 feet, Titan Hanover's at 22 feet.

10. The United States Trotting Association.

11. An association of harness race tracks and racing associations in the most important centers of harness racing with,

generally, fixed purses and uniform conditions; comparable to the "big" leagues in baseball.

12. Six specific conditions for registration are listed in the rules of the U.S.T.A.; summarized, these require:

   (a) A registered standardbred sire and dam

                         or

   (b) A registered standardbred sire; a dam (and grand-dam) sired by a standardbred horse; a Standard record; and being the sire or dam of two or more performers with Standard records. (There are four specific requirements under this general classification—one for stallions, three for mares.)

                         or

   (c) The approval of a specially appointed committee of breeders.

13. A record mile of 2:30 trotting or 2:25 pacing. This was "Standard."

14. The four high wheeled "wagon."

15. Ohio. New York, Illinois, and Pennsylvania follow in that order.

16. Ohio.

17. New York—based on weeks of racing.

18. France, Italy, Germany, Australia, New Zealand, Holland, Sweden, Belgium, Russia.

19. The Hambletonian, Kentucky Futurity, and Yonkers Futurity.

20. Lexington, Kentucky, was for a long time and probably still is. New York City, with nearby Roosevelt and Yonkers Raceways very active and with big purses, might well press the claim.

21. Orange County, New York.

22. Counterclockwise.

23. A race open to horses named by a committee or specially designated person (classifier). The horses are selected because of their presumed ability to compete on an equal basis.

24. A race not limited by time or money winning classification —and hence classic events in which, as a rule, only the fastest horses are entered.

25. A race in which the entries are limited to horses which have won less than $24,000.

26. Since World War II, with the substantial growth of pari-mutuel raceways, there has been a marked trend to single-dash races instead of the traditional two out of three heats.

27. Trotting or pacing in hand to the start, preparatory to starting a race. Also refers to brief warm up dashes prior to the start.

28. A short dash at top speed, generally on approaching the finish. Formerly, the term also described the short informal races between two or more road drivers, popular on the highways and speedways up to the turn of the century.

29. Refers to a horse sulking and not doing his best in a race.

30. A half mile track.

31. Not at all.

32. ⅖ of a second, and only by just less than ⅖ of a second since 1905!

33. 1834 by Edwin Forrest (2:31½).

34. 1843 by both Lady Suffolk and Beppo (2:28).

35. 1859 by Flora Temple (2:19¾).

36. 1884 by Jay Eye See (2:10) and Maud S. (2:09¾).

37. 1897, August 28; the time was 1:59¼.

38. Star Pointer, a pacer, at Readville, Mass.

39. 1903; the time was 2:00.

40. Lou Dillon, at Readville, Mass. In the same year, at Memphis, she trotted a mile in 1:58½.

41. 2:20; the record was 2:17¼.

42. 2:05; the record was 2:03¼.

43. 2:00; the record was 1:58.

44. 2:00.

45. 1:55¼ by Greyhound on September 29, 1938, at Lexington, Ky.

46. 1:54⅗ set by ADIOS BUTLER on October 4, 1960 at Lexington, Kentucky.

47. The males seem to have it. Since Nancy Hanks' 2:04 mile in 1892, 7 out of 9 new records have been established by stallions or geldings. In 37 Hambletonians, only 10 fillies have won.

48. They were made against time rather than in a race and, most important, behind a running horse and a shield to eliminate wind resistance.

49. The Hambletonian Stake.

50. The Hambletonian Stake.

51. The Westbury Futurity or Horseman Stake.

52. The Fox Stake or Roosevelt Futurity.

53. The Little Brown Jug, the Messenger, or the Cane Futurity.

54. The Transylvania Stake at Lexington, Kentucky, first trotted in 1889.

55. No. Not generally.

56. (a) That the entry be a registered Standardbred nominated as a yearling prior to May 1 with the payment of a $10 fee.

    (b) That additional fees be paid as follows:

        (1) $200 on the 1st of January following nomination.

        (2) $250 on the next 1st of January (the second following nomination) and

        (3) $1,500 starting fee.

57. 58 minutes, 21 seconds, by BLACKROD, driven by R. L. Parker at Aiken, S. C. in 1942—against time.

58. 1826—on May 16, at Centerville, Long Island, N. Y.

59. 157 at the close of the 1963 season.

60. 497 at the close of the 1963 season.

61. The mobile starting gate mounted on an automobile chassis. There are several types.

62. A pacer.

63. Sandshifter, Wiggler and, of course, Sidewheeler.

64. Leather straps looped about each pair of a horse's lateral legs to cause him to pace.

65. Yes.

66. Weighted shoes.

67. Quarter boots (bell, hinged and close fitting)—as a protection from overreaching.

68. About 30 pounds. 32 is usual, but some as light as 26 pounds have been used.

69. 1892.

70. The driver's seat was lowered to the level of the shafts, further to reduce wind resistance.

71. The major items include:
    Breast collar (traces)
    "Saddle"
    Girth
    Thimbles
    Tug Straps
    Crupper (crupper strap)
    Overcheck

72. The driver, the sulky, shoeing, the track, the weather.

73. That is was made on a KITE shaped track. Records made by the same horse on a kite shaped track were about 2 seconds faster than on an oval track. This was due to the elimination of turns, rounding which the high wheeled sulkies of the time skidded, thus reducing their speed.

74. 1½ miles is the greatest distance raced with any frequency today.

75. Owner of the famous sire Hambletonian.

76. Queen of the trotters in the decade 1850 to 1860, she was the first harness horse to go a mile in 2:20 or better (2:19¾ in 1859) when she was 14 years old, breaking her own 4-year-old record. The 2:19¾ record stood for 8 years.

77. An outstanding pacer, in 1905 he established a mile record of 1:55¼ (behind a windshield) which stood for 33 years before it was lowered by a quarter second to 1:55—without a windshield, however.

78. Winner of the 1935 Hambletonian, he holds the trotting record for a mile and the fastest mile under saddle. He was

also noted for his height, 16.1¼, and the fact that he was an unprepossessing yearling, sold for $800.

79. Generally agreed upon are: Hambletonian, Black Hawk, Justin Morgan, Bellfounder, Henry Clay, Mambrino Chief, Pilot, Jr., Electioneer, Volunteer.

80. MESSENGER is Hambletonian's GREAT GRAND SIRE. Hambletonian is descended from Messenger through both his sire, Abdallah and his dam, The Kent Mare.

Polo

P.B.

AVERAGE SCORES:

(Per cent answered correctly)

5 who ride but do not play polo	30
5 who do not ride but have witnessed polo	22
5 polo players handicapped at 0	62
3 players handicapped in excess of 5	91

To determine your score (or anyone else's), count the number of questions answered correctly and consult the table on pages 225 and 226.

The answers to the questions in this section will be found following the list of questions, on pages 172 through 178.

POLO

QUESTIONS

1. What is the correct term for what is commonly referred to as a "chukker"?

2. What is its duration?

3. What is the maximum duration of play?

4. By what other name is the No. 4 position generally referred to?

5. Which position is generally referred to as the pivot?

6. What are the standard dimensions of a boarded polo field?

7. What is the width of the goal?

8. Of what is a polo ball made?

9. Which is larger, a polo ball or a baseball?

10. Which is heavier?

11. Name three woods of which the mallet head is usually made.

12. Name two woods of which the mallet shaft is usually made.

13. What, approximately, is the usual weight of a mallet?

14. How should a wooden mallet be hung when not in use?

15. What is the purpose of the small rubber rings near the head of some mallet shafts?

16. Name three qualities or characteristics of a mallet which vary with the selection of individual players, other than the materials from which it is made.

17. What is the difference between an umpire and a referee?

18. For what purpose should an umpire blow his whistle?

19. What is a "safety"?

20. What is the penalty for a "safety"?

21. What is Penalty Number One?

22. How many *penalties* are there for infractions of the rules and for fouls?

23. Name four fouls.

24. Prior to 1936, what was the usual penalty inflicted for a foul in indoor polo?

25. Is the mount generally used for polo a pony?

26. What, approximately, is the average height of a polo mount?

27. What, approximately, is the range in weight of middle-weight polo mounts?

28. Name three of the most desirable characteristics with respect to the performance of a polo mount.

29. With regard to type, what is the usual breeding of good polo mounts?

30. At what age, as a rule, do polo mounts begin tournament play?

31. In which countries, other than the United States, are a large number of the polo mounts used in the United States bred?

32. In which country is the greatest number of polo mounts bred?

33. In which state is the greatest number of polo mounts bred?

34. Do polo mounts instinctively follow the ball?

35. What limitation has there been with regard to the height of polo mounts?

36. What is the highest price paid for a polo mount at a public sale?

37. On which is a polo mount habitually turned, the forehand or hind quarters?

38. What distinctive protective device is worn on the legs of polo mounts?

39. What is the difference between the shoeing of the front and hind feet of a polo mount?

40. What prohibition is there with regard to spurs?

41. What is considered the best grass for polo field turf in the northern United States?

42. Approximately how far does the average long drive of a high goal player travel?

43. What is the origin of the name polo?

44. Where is the game of polo generally considered to have originated?

45. Where was the "center" of polo in the United States: (a) in the 1880s and '90s, (b) in the 1920s, and (c) now?

46. By whom was polo introduced into the United States?

47. When?

48. Where?

49. Approximately how many players appear on the handicap list of the United States Polo Association?

50. Which of the seven circuits has the greatest number of regular member clubs?

51. Which would indicate the better player—one handicapped at 4 or one at 6?

52. What is the greatest number of players handicapped at 10 goals at one time in the United States?

53. Approximately what percentage of players are handicapped at 0?

54. Approximately how many players have handicaps of 6 goals or more?

55. Where and in what year was the first match for the Westchester ("International") Cup between Great Britain and the United States played?

56. How many matches (series of games) have been won by the United States?

57. When did England last win possession of the cup?

58. When did the United States first win it?

59. Who were the original "Big Four"?

60. In what year was the Senior Championship tournament last played?

61. What national championship tournaments (outdoor) are conducted annually by the U.S. Polo Association?

62. Has any team won both the Junior (now Twenty Goal) and Open Championship in the same year? If so, which?

63. The winner of which national tournament is considered the champion team of the United States?

64. The same high goal teams have frequently been entered in both the Open Championship and the Monty Waterbury Memorial Cup tournament. In what respect does the former differ from the latter?

65. Name six commonly used strokes.

66. Of the various strokes used in a game by all of the players, approximately what percentage are the offside forward stroke?

67. What is characteristic of the stroking of native Indian players?

68. What is the difference between the headgear generally worn by American and English players?

69. How were fouls penalized prior to 1920?

70. Prior to 1924, what limitation was there on left-handed players?

71. In the early days of polo in the United States, what was the method of starting the game?

72. What is the chief difference between the martingale used for polo and that frequently used for hunting?

73. What is a "round robin"?

74. For Arena Polo, what are the dimensions of a standard arena?

75. How wide is the goal (distance between the insides of the goal posts) in a standard arena?

76. What Arena championship tournaments are conducted annually by the U.S. Polo Association?

Examine the following sketches:

77. Is this a foul? On whom?

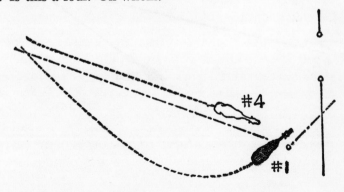

78. Is this a foul? On whom?

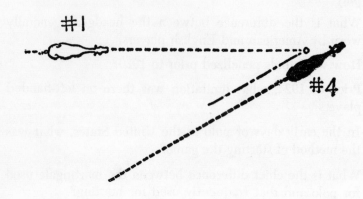

79. Who has the right of way?

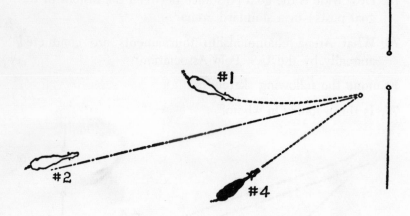

80. Who has the right of way?

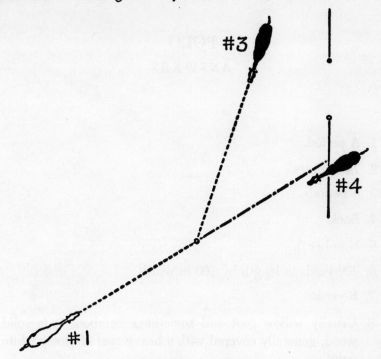

POLO

ANSWERS

1. A period.

2. 7½ minutes.

3. 8 periods.

4. Back.

5. Number 3.

6. 300 yards in length by 160 in width.

7. 8 yards.

8. Usually willow root and sometimes bamboo. It is solid wood, generally covered with a heavy coat of glossy white paint.

9. A polo ball, by slightly over a quarter of an inch in diameter.

10. A baseball, by slightly over a half ounce.

11. Maple, bamboo, sycamore, ash, and elm are used.

12. Long or short jointed tapered cane, malacca, and moonah are usual.

13. Approximately 1 pound; it ranges from 15 to 18 ounces.

14. By the thong, with the head down, to prevent the shaft from warping unduly.

15. To prevent the shaft from being broken by a ball striking the mallet at this weak point.

16. Length; weight; degree, and point of greatest "whippiness"; shape of the head; number of joints in the shaft; shape and binding of the handle.

17. The umpire is the mounted official on the field. In important matches there are two umpires and a referee, not mounted and off the field, who renders the final decision in the event the umpires disagree.

18. Only to stop play.

19. A ball hit behind its back line by one of the defending side.

20. A free hit by the attacking side, sixty yards from the back line (goal line or goal line extended), opposite the point where the ball crossed the back line; none of the side fouling to be within 30 yards of the ball.

21. The award of a goal to the side fouled, plus a free hit at goal from the 40-yard line.

22. Eleven.

23. The fouls are infringements of the field rules. In general they are: (The list is, of course, not complete or detailed.)
    (a) Delaying the game unnecessarily.
    (b) Crossing a player who has the right of way at a distance which might cause a collision or be dangerous.
    (c) Pulling across the line of the ball so as to endanger oneself or the player who has the right of way.
    (d) Not giving way to a player who has the right of way when riding from a different direction or not giving way to two players approaching from an opposite direction.
    (e) Dangerous riding, such as bumping at a dangerous angle, zigzagging in front of another player who is at a gallop, pulling across another horse's forelegs, riding an

opponent across the line of the ball, stopping or pulling up on the ball.

(f) Rough play, such as seizing another player or his pony with the hand, striking or pushing with the head, hand, arm, or elbow.

(g) Dangerous and illegal use of the mallet, such as hooking an opponent's mallet other than from directly behind or on the same side of the opponent's pony as the ball; reaching across, over or under any part of any opponent's pony to strike the ball or hook his mallet; intentionally striking an opponent's or one's own pony with a mallet.

(h) Catching or carrying the ball (except momentarily) or striking the ball with anything but the mallet.

24. The deduction of a half-point from the score of the side committing the foul.

25. Generally not; he is a small horse.

26. Approximately 15.1 hands; they range from 14.3 to 15.3.

27. From 900 to 1,100 pounds.

28. Speed, handiness, stamina.

29. Thoroughbred or largely Thoroughbred. For many years the best polo mounts were generally produced from Thoroughbred sires out of polo playing mares, or mares of polo type, which were not necessarily purebred Thoroughbreds, with the Thoroughbred strain thus seldom in excess of ¾ or ⅞. The thought was that a purebred Thoroughbred was too "hot" and not sufficiently handy for polo. In recent years, however, there is a tendency, in high goal polo, to play Thoroughbreds almost exclusively—understandable, with the great emphasis on speed.

30. Generally at six years; often, and desirably, at seven, and occasionally, but not desirably, at five.

31. In Argentina and England.

32. In the United States.

33. Texas. (Reliable data is, however, not available.)

34. No. They are very sensitive to their riders' shift in weight and change in attitude and to the use of the aids—and thus *appear* to "follow the ball." Roll a ball in sight of a polo mount untacked in a paddock, and he will ignore it.

35. Prior to 1915, the height was limited by the U. S. Polo Association to 14.2 hands, when it was changed to 15.1. Since 1920 there has been no limitation with regard to the height of mounts.

36. $22,000 by Stephen Sanford, for Lewis L. Lacey's Jupiter, at the auction of the Argentine team's ponies in 1928.

37. The hind quarters.

38. Felt "boots" or bandages covering the fetlock (ankle) and extending a short way up the cannon; usually on the fore-legs, and sometimes also on the hind legs.

39. The front shoes have no calks; the hind shoes are calked.

40. Sharp spurs are prohibited.

41. In the northern United States and in California, almost equal parts of (1) Chewing Fescue, (2) Colonial Bent, (3) Kentucky Blue, and (4) Fancy Red Top. (In the south-east, where water is not readily available, Bermuda grass is often used.)

42. Approximately 100 yards. Recent "records" are about 160 yards.

43. It is an adaptation of the Tibetan word "Pulu" meaning a ball.

44. In Persia; written records and drawings indicate that a contest between mounted men and women equipped each with a mallet for stroking a ball through goal posts, known apparently as "chaugán," was popular at court as early as 590 A.D. Records also indicate that the game was known to the ancient Greeks, the Persians, and the Chinese before the Christian Era. The game was common in India in the 16th Century.

45. (a) New York (the Polo Grounds) and Newport, Rhode Island; (b) the Meadow Brook Club on Long Island, New York; (c) the Oak Brook Polo Club in Hinsdale, Illinois.

46. James Gordon Bennett.

47. In 1876.

48. New York City, indoors, in Dickel's Riding Academy at Fifth Avenue and Thirty-ninth Street.

49. Approximately 700.

50. The Pacific Coast Circuit.

51. One handicapped at 6.

52. Five. In 1917 and 1918, Devereaux Milburn, Harry Payne Whitney, Foxhall Keene, J. M. Waterbury, and Lawrence Waterbury.

53. Approximately 40 per cent.

54. About 25. The number varies, of course, from year to year, but not much from this figure.

55. At Newport, Rhode Island in August 1886.

56. Nine (out of twelve).

57. In 1914.

58. In 1909.

59. Lawrence Waterbury, J. M. ("Monty") Waterbury, Harry Payne Whitney, and Devereaux Milburn.

60. In 1921.

61. Four. The Open, Twenty Goal, Inter-Circuit, and Twelve Goal.

62. Yes, Midwick in 1924 with E. G. Miller, Eric L. Pedley, Arthur P. Perkins, and Carlton F. Burke.

63. The winner of the Open Championship tournament.

64. The Open Championship is played "on the flat," i.e. without handicap allowance. The Waterbury Cup tournament is played with handicap allowances.

65. (a) Offside forward, (b) Offside back.
    (c) Nearside forward, (d) Nearside back.
    (e) Under the neck, from the offside.
    (f) Under the neck, from the nearside.
    (g) Under the tail from the offside.
    (h) Under the tail, from the nearside.

66. About 75 per cent.

67. It is executed largely with a snap of the wrist, the mallet being very "whippy."

68. The American habitually wears a polo "cap," while the Englishman generally wears a "helmet" similar to the sun helmet worn in the tropics and Far East.

69. The deduction of a ½ point from the score of the side fouling. A "safety" incurred the deduction of ¼ point.

70. They were prohibited, unless registered as such with the U. S. Polo Association.

71. A rider from each side dashed at the ball, placed in the center of the field, from his respective end of it.

72. That used for polo is a standing martingale, i.e., the upper end is attached to the cavesson nose band; that generally used for hunting is a running martingale, the upper ends terminating in two metal rings through which the reins pass.

73. A polo match in which three teams compete on the same field in one event, consisting of three matches of two, three and sometimes four periods each. For example, A plays B, B plays C, and A plays C. The winner is the team which has the best record of matches won or tied—or the one having the greatest number of net goals to its credit.

74. 300 by 150 feet.

75. 10 feet.

76. Six. The Open, Senior or High Goal, Twelve Goal, Sherman Memorial, Intercollegiate, and Preparatory School Championships.

77. Yes, on the Black Number 1 for crossing; although he hit the ball last, he loses the right of way because the White Back has ridden on a line closer and more nearly parallel to the line on which the ball is traveling.

78. No, the Black Back has crossed the White Number 1, who has the right of way, at a distance which does not involve the possibility of collision or danger.

79. The White Number 1. He has followed more closely the line on which the ball is traveling.

80. The White Number 1. He is on the line the ball is traveling even though he is approaching in an opposite direction; the Black Number 3 would cross the line and must give way.

Cowboys and the West

AVERAGE SCORES:

(Per cent answered correctly)

5 who ride but have never visited a ranch, dude or other, or attended a rodeo	31
5 who do not ride but who have attended a rodeo	52
5 who have ridden on a cattle ranch	77
3 "cowboys"	92

To determine your score (or anyone else's), count the number of questions answered correctly and consult the table on pages 225 and 226.

The answers to the questions in this section will be found following the list of questions, on pages 186 through 193.

COWBOYS AND THE WEST
QUESTIONS

1. What is a "bronc"?

2. What is the derivation of the term "bronc"?

3. What is a "broke" horse?

4. What is an "outlaw"?

5. What is a "broomtail"?

6. What is a "pinto"?

7. What is a "remuda"?

8. What is the correct name for the horse commonly used by cattlemen on the western plains?

9. What is the average (or typical) height of these horses?

10. What are two typical characteristics of the western "cow pony," other than height, weight or conformation?

11. What type of horse predominates among those bred in the West for market?

12. In what state is the greatest number of horses raised?

13. What animal, in the mountains bordering the southwestern plains, is the horse's greatest and most dangerous enemy?

14. What is a "maverick"?

15. What is a "dogie"?

16. What is the purpose of a "round up"?

17. What is meant by "cutting out" calves?

18. What is meant by "riding herd"?

19. What is a "buckaroo"?

20. What is a "critter"?

21. What is a "steer"?

22. What type or breed of beef cattle is predominant on the western plains today?

23. What was it 50 years ago?

24. In which state is the greatest number of beef cattle raised?

25. What is the chief difference between the cattle raised in the northwest and the southwest?

26. What animals, in addition to horses and beef cattle, are raised in large numbers on the western plains?

27. Why did the horse and beef cattlemen dislike and oppose the ranging of these other animals in their country?

28. Of what, in general, are the fences found on the western plains constructed?

29. Since the horses used on the western ranches are not as a rule jumped, how do cowhands get their horses on the other side of a fence when they are not near a gate?

30. What is a "chuck" wagon?

31. What is a "wrangler"?

32. What is a "dude"?

33. What is a "rustler"?

34. If you were lost in the cattle country of the West, what, besides the sun, would be your most likely guide in day time?

35. What is an "arroyo"?

36. What is the Mexican name for "cowboy"?

37. In what chief respect is the "seat" of the western cattlemen different from that generally used by hunting men?

38. Why is it that a cowhand's bridle reins are not fastened together?

39. How is the head stall (top part of the bridle) of a typical cow pony's bridle held in place?

40. What is the correct name for the saddle used by cattlemen in the West?

41. What is a "center fire rig"?

42. What is the primary use of the prominent pommel horn on the cattleman's saddle?

43. What part of a stock saddle is a "fender"?

44. What is a "hobble"?

45. Why does a cowhand wear high-heeled boots?

46. What does a cowhand in the Southwest instinctively do to his boots before pulling them on?

47. What is the correct name for "chaps" and for what are they used?

48. What practical use is made of the cattleman's neckerchief?

49. What is a "lariat"?

50. By what other name is the lariat frequently known?

51. What, approximately, is the usual length of the cowhand's rope?

52. What is the diameter of the rope most commonly used?

53. Of what is it made?

54. What is a "honda"?

55. What is the origin of the rodeo?

56. What is the derivation of the word "rodeo"?

57. What is a "chute"?

58. What is meant by "sunfishing"?

59. What device attached to the saddle is used to stimulate or promote the bucking of horses in rodeos?

60. What is meant by "scratching"?

61. Name FOUR contests usually included in a rodeo program.

62. What is "bulldogging"?

63. How long is a bronc rider required to stay on a bucking horse?

64. What is a "hazer"?

65. What is a "pick up man"?

66. Where and in what year were cash prizes first awarded at a rodeo?

67. Where and in what year were spectators first charged admission at a rodeo?

68. What is the governing body of rodeos?

69. What is the basis for classifying rodeos?

70. How is the year's champion of a rodeo event determined?

71. What are "levis"?

72. What is a "tapadero"?

73. What is especially distinctive about the stockman's spurs?

74. What was the "Pony Express"?

75. Name two famous painters of Western scenes, horses and men.

76. Who is Will James?

77. What is the surname of "Buffalo Bill," the famous Indian fighter?

78. Name two foreign countries especially noted for their cattle and horses.

79. What characteristic quality of a good cow pony is also highly desirable in a polo pony?

80. What is a "Quarter Horse"?

COWBOYS AND THE WEST

ANSWERS

1. An unbroken or untamed horse, or a horse that, although it has been broken and ridden, remains mean, dangerous and untrustworthy. (The term is also sometimes used to describe a western "cow pony," whether broken or unbroken, without regard to its "orneriness.")

2. From the Spanish "bronco," meaning "wild," "untamed."

3. A horse that is sufficiently manageable to bridle, saddle and ride with reasonable safety.

4. A vicious horse that cannot be ridden with safety, regularly or periodically devoting its energies to unseating or disposing of its rider.

5. A small, wild horse not worth the bother of "breaking" or training—sometimes a horse of inferior breeding or quality.

6. A piebald or skewbald horse; one with a coat of dark hair marked with large spots or splotches of white.

7. A collection of "broken" horses, in a corral or assembled on the plain, from which the horses to be ridden in the day's work are selected. Also, a "string" of horses assigned to a cowhand.

8. A range horse.

9. Approximately 15 hands. They range generally from 14 to 15 hands in the southwest—and to 16 hands and over in the northwest.

10. He is handy, sure-footed, hardy.

11. Quarter Horses largely—and also Arabians, Appaloosas and Palominos.

12. Texas. Missouri is second, Kentucky third.

13. The mountain lion (cougar).

14. An unbranded calf.

15. Originally a motherless calf, but now frequently applied to young scrub cattle of poor quality.

16. To take inventory of the stock, to brand young calves and horses, and to select stock for shipment to market.

17. To separate a special group of calves from the herd by "hazing" them into a position (on a cutting pony) to be roped (by another hand on a rope pony) and taken out of the herd; usually applied to separating unbranded calves preparatory to tying them down for branding.

18. Riding slowly around the herd to prevent any of the animals straying from it, to drive back stragglers and to prevent a stampede.

19. A hard riding cowhand whose chief occupation is breaking broncs. Sometimes also applied to rodeo riders.

20. A calf; the term is, however, frequently applied to range cattle generally.

21. A castrated male of the beef cattle raised on the western plains.

22. Hereford.

23. The "Long Horn," a long horned variety of only fair beef cattle which migrated north from old Mexico. It is now almost extinct.

24. Texas. Then Oklahoma, Nebraska, Kansas, South Dakota, and Iowa in that order.

25. The Hereford predominates in both the north and the south; in the north, however, these cattle are larger and heavier.

26. Sheep.

27. Because they nibble the grass so short as to make it entirely useless for grazing cattle and horses, and because their small sharp hoofs cut the grass into the ground and kill it.

28. Barbed wire.

29. By "laying" the fence. In a length of fence, several of the posts are not driven into the ground, so that a section of it may be turned and laid on the ground. The horse is led over this section of the fence.

30. A horse-drawn commissary and supply wagon, in which food, cooking utensils, fuel, and a crude stove are carried to furnish meals (in the southwest largely Frijole beans and biscuit) to the men working on the plains. "Chuck" is the term applied to food. (Compare the Army's "chow.")

31. A hand whose duty is to watch and periodically assemble the "remuda" of horses for the others engaged in work on the plains.

32. Anyone not a native of the West; originally one who dressed in a fashion not customary on the range and who was strange to the ways and customs of the range. Now frequently used to describe a paying guest at a western ranch.

33. A cattle or horse thief.

34. A fence or a stream. (If you can find either.)

35. A dried-up stream bed.

36. Vaquero.

37. His stirrups are very long and his entire body is nearly vertical, giving the effect of standing on the stirrups, with perhaps the support of the cantle. This is due to the type saddle he rides with its relatively narrow space between a high pommel and cantle and with stirrups hung from the middle of the saddle.

38. So that when he dismounts or is thrown the reins will fall with the loose ends lying on the ground; then if the horse attempts to move away, it will step on the loose ends of the reins, apply pressure with the bit and stop itself. (There is generally nothing on the plains to which a horse may be tied.)

39. By a slit in the head stall through which the near ear is passed.

40. A stock saddle.

41. A single cinch encircling the horse from a point midway between the pommel horn and cantle of the saddle as opposed to the more usual double girths.

42. To provide an "anchor" to which the end of the lariat is secured—either before or after an animal has been roped (a rope, before—a rawhide reata, after.)

43. An oblong piece of leather attached to the stirrup leather of a stock saddle to protect the rider's legs.

44. A device for fastening together a horse's forelegs, to fetter him. It is usually composed of two straps buckled just above the fetlocks and fastened together by a short strap or chain; sometimes it is merely a rawhide tie and occasionally, as a makeshift, rope is used.

45. To provide a secure hold and firm footing in the ground

(by digging the heels in) when roping from the ground, and also to prevent his feet slipping through the stirrups, thus avoiding the possibility of being hung up on a bad horse.

46. He turns them upside down and taps the soles vigorously— to rid them of a tarantula, lizard, snake, or other objectionable creature that may have wandered in.

47. Chaparajos (pronounced Chá pa-rá hos). They protect the legs from thorny or heavy brush and from severe weather.

48. It is used to lift over the nose and mouth as a protection from the dust, and in the North to tie over the ears in winter.

49. A rope of small diameter with a running noose, carried on the cowhand's saddle, used for catching or securing cattle or horses.

50. Lasso.

51. 30 or 35 feet.

52. ⅜ to ½ an inch, usually ⁷⁄₁₆.

53. Hemp is traditional and still largely used by experienced hands, but silk manila, silk sisal, and waxed nylon are also much used and growing in popularity.

54. A metal eye which fits inside the loop at the end of a lariat through which the other end is passed to form a running noose.

55. The rodeo originated in the days of the unfenced ranges in the '70s. A kind of country fair was held following the semi-annual round ups, at which the cowhands of the several ranches, after they were paid off, incidentally entertained themselves with feats of skill and informal contests in connection with their work, as well as progressive poker

and the droning of ballads. These affairs gradually developed into local "shows" or exhibitions.

56. From the Spanish for "round up."

57. A narrow, wooden, boxlike enclosure, in which horses (so that they may be saddled and mounted) and cattle are placed awaiting their turns and from which they are released to take part in rodeo events. On the ranch it is used for branding, veterinary attention, etc.

58. The motion of a bucking horse, characterized by swaying and twisting from side to side as he jumps so that his forefeet land alternately on opposite sides of the line of his progress, which causes particular difficulty to the rider.

59. The "bucking cinch" or "flank cinch," a strap of leather or webbing encircling his belly well to the rear.

60. A rider, on a bucking bronc, spurring his mount alternately on the flanks and shoulders.

61. They include at least: saddle bronc riding, bareback bronc riding, steer riding, steer wrestling, calf roping, steer decorating, steer roping, and team roping.

62. Steer wrestling, a rodeo event in which a rider endeavors to "throw" a heavy steer in the shortest time by leaping from his horse, catching the steer by the horns and through sheer weight and strength twisting the steer's head around until the animal falls to the ground on its side.

63. 10 seconds on saddle broncs, 8 seconds bareback.

64. A rider who assists a bulldogging contestant by galloping on the opposite side of the steer to keep it from veering away when the contestant slips out of his saddle.

65. A mounted ring assistant who releases the bucking cinch and lifts bronc riding contestants off their bucking horses when the time limit has expired.

66. At Pecos, Texas, in 1883.

67. At Prescott, Arizona, in 1888.

68. The Rodeo Cowboy's Association.

69. The amount of prize money offered.

70. The designation is awarded to the contestant amassing the greatest number of points during the year. One point is awarded for each dollar of prize money won.

71. Blue denim jeans, rather tight legged with riveted seam points, usually worn by stockmen at work. Those made by Levi Straus of San Francisco were very popular—hence the term.

72. A long, pointed leather hood covering the stirrup of a stock saddle. This:

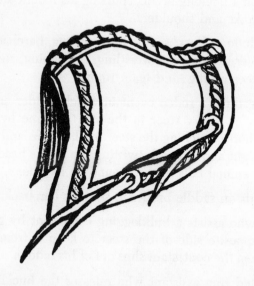

73. The shank terminates in a large rowel—a thin "wheel" the circumference of which consists of a succession of pointed metal spokes. This is what they look like:

74. A private company which operated a relay of horses by which mail was carried from St. Joseph, Missouri, to San Francisco, California, and vice versa, before railroads were extended across the continent.

75. The best-known are Charles M. Russell, Frederic Remington, William Ziegler, Pete Martinez, Burris Jenkins, Frank Hoffman, William R. Leigh and Olaf Weighorst.

76. A well-known cowboy artist and author.

77. Cody.

78. Argentina and Canada.

79. Handiness—the ability to stop and turn quickly, and to change direction on the correct lead—quick response to "neck reining."

80. A registered breed of western U. S. horse much used for working stock. It is characterized by a notable burst of speed at short distances—about a quarter mile. Thus the name. He is relatively short, "built low to the ground," with thick short cannons, well muscled and stocky. The breed originated in Virginia in the 1760's.

The Cavalry

AVERAGE SCORES:

(Per cent answered correctly)

5 who ride but have never been in the Army   20

5 who were or are enlisted in the National Guard Cavalry   42

5 Second Lieutenants of Cavalry, National Guard and Organized Reserves   71

5 Captains of Cavalry, National Guard and Organized Reserves   84

5 Cavalry Officers of the Regular Army   95

To determine your score (or anyone else's), count the number of questions answered correctly and consult the table on pages 225 and 226.

The answers to the questions in this section will be found following the list of questions, on pages 202 through 208.

THE CAVALRY

QUESTIONS

1. What was the United States Cavalry insignia?

2. What was the United States Cavalry color?

3. What are the national and regimental flags carried by mounted organizations called?

4. Did the United States Army always include the cavalry prior to World War II?

5. When was the 1st United States Cavalry (Regiment) organized?

6. By what other names have cavalry troops in the United States Army been known?

7. What are Hussars?

8. What are Dragoons?

9. What are Lancers?

10. Was any mounted United States Cavalry in action overseas during World War I? If so, what was it?

11. During World War II? If so, what was it?

12. Was there any horse cavalry in the U. S. during World War II?

13. Name five general officers who in that rank were in direct command of United States Cavalry troops in wartime prior to World War I.

14. Name three general officers who in that rank were in direct command of Confederate Cavalry.

15. Name two general officers who were in direct command of Allied cavalry troops in mounted combat during World War I.

16. Which of the following World War II generals was a cavalryman? MacArthur, Omar Bradley, Wainwright, Mark Clark?

17. Of our World War II divisions, approximately how many were commanded by cavalrymen?

18. Name three former cavalrymen who commanded a corps, its equivalent or higher organization in World War II.

19. Name three famous battles or campaigns in which cavalry had a dominant role. (Throughout history.)

20. Where was the United States Cavalry School?

21. Where was the Cavalry School of Italy?

22. Of France?

23. Of Germany?

24. Of England? (The senior mounted service school?)

25. Of Austria?

26. Name a famous poem concerning the valor of a cavalry action.

27. Prior to World War II, how many Regular Army cavalry regiments were there?

28. How many regular Army cavalry divisions?

29. How many active National Guard cavalry divisions?

30. What were the numerical designations of the regiments in the 1st Cavalry Division at the beginning of World War II?

31. What was the role of the 1st Cavalry Division in World War II?

32. By what name was the saddle used by the United States Cavalry trooper usually referred to?

33. In what way did the saddle used by United States Cavalry officers differ from the trooper's saddle, and what is the name of the former?

34. Approximately how many officers and men were there in a war strength cavalry division?

35. In a war strength horse cavalry regiment?

36. In a war strength horse troop? (Rifle.)

37. In a war strength rifle platoon, horse?

38. What unit in the infantry corresponds to a cavalry troop?

39. What unit in the field artillery corresponds to a cavalry troop?

40. What was the unit next higher than a troop in the organization of cavalry?

41. What in general were the chief missions of cavalry?

42. What were the chief characteristics of cavalry?

43. What is a remount?

44. What in general was the breeding (type) of United States Cavalry mounts?

45. Where in general were United States Army riding mounts procured?

46. What was the average price paid by the government for Army mounts?

47. What was the average height of typical Army riding mounts?

48. What was the average weight of typical Army riding mounts?

49. How were Army mounts identified?

50. What was the weight of the mounted trooper's pack?

51. Where was it carried?

52. What was the maximum prescribed load for a United States Cavalry pack horse?

53. With what weapons was the mounted cavalry (rifle) trooper habitually armed?

54. What other weapons were used by the United States Cavalry, excluding mechanized vehicles?

55. What was the longest peace-time march made in a day by horse cavalry with full equipment, terminating with the command in good condition?

56. What was considered a satisfactory day's march for trained horse cavalry with full equipment?

57. At approximately what average rate (miles per hour) would such a march have been made?

58. At what gaits?

59. At what rate (miles per hour) were cavalry horses trained to walk?

60. To trot?

61. To gallop, collected?

62. What in general is the rate of the extended gallop? (Cavalry mounts.)

63. How many minutes, in an hour other than the first or last, would you trot to proceed at a rate of six miles per hour on a good road?

64. Assuming suitable terrain, prepare a march schedule for marching six miles per hour. (Other than the first or last hour.)

65. Where, relative to the location of other elements in bivouac, was the picket line placed?

66. What were the chief duties of the stable sergeant?

67. Who was the last chief of cavalry?

68. Who was the first?

69. How many Chiefs of Staff of the Army have been cavalrymen?

70. Approximately how many mules did the Army have?

71. Where did it get them?

72. What use was made of them?

73. What was the intermediary or preliminary stage in the transformation of horse cavalry to mechanized cavalry?

74. During World War II, what change was made in the designation and organization of mechanized cavalry regiments?

75. Name three types of unit to which cavalry regiments were converted when, during World War II, horse cavalry regiments lost their horses.

76. To what were cavalry regiments converted in World War I?

77. How many remount stations were operated by the Army?

78. Name them.

79. By what branch of the Army were they administered?

80. What, if any, is the organic cavalry component of an infantry division?

THE CAVALRY

1. Crossed sabers (the hilt down).

2. Yellow.

3. Standards. Carried by foot troops they are called colors.

4. No. Mounted troops were not continuously maintained as part of our army until 1833. Such mounted troops as were organized prior to this time were generally known as Dragoons. The three regiments of cavalry and one of dragoons authorized by Congress shortly after the independence of the U. S. were never at their authorized strength and were subsequently disbanded, so that between 1802 and the beginning of the War of 1812 our army contained no mounted troops. The two regiments of dragoons authorized, and to some extent organized just prior to the War of 1812, were disbanded in 1815.

5. In 1833, as the Regiment of Dragoons; its name was changed to the 1st U. S. Cavalry (Regiment) in 1861. The present 4th Cavalry was designated the 1st Cavalry, in 1855, its designation being changed back to the 4th Cavalry in 1861.

6. Dragoons and Mounted Rifles.

7. Light cavalry, armed with the saber and often distinguished by brilliant uniforms.

8. Cavalry equipped for and often fighting on foot; at one time mounted infantry.

9. Light cavalry, armed with the lance.

10. Yes. A provisional squadron of the 2nd Cavalry was in action during the St. Mihiel and Meuse-Argonne operations.

11. Yes. The 26th U. S. Cavalry (Philippine Scouts) on Bataan, P. I.

12. Yes—the 1st and 2nd Cavalry Divisions until they left for overseas assignments and the 112th and 124th Regiments.

13. * Averill, Buford, Custer, Gregg, Grierson, Kilpatrick, Mackenzie, Merritt, Pleasanton, Sheridan, Stoneman, Wilson.

14. *Forrest, Fitzhugh Lee, W. H. F. ("Rooney") Lee, Morgan, Rosser, Stuart, Wheeler.

15. † Allenby, Chavel, Conneau, Hamilton, Sordet.

16. Wainwright.

17. 30—2 Cavalry, 13 Armored, 14 Infantry, 1 Philippine Scout.

18. W. D. Crittenberger, E. N. Harmon, Kenyon Joyce, Geoffrey Keyes, Ben Lear, John Milliken, George S. Patton, Innis P. Swift, Lucian K. Truscott, Jonathan M. Wainwright.

19. † The campaigns of Philip, Alexander, Hannibal, Attila, Genghis Khan, Gustavus Adolphus, Marlborough, Frederick and the Crusaders.
Cannae.
Pursuit by Napoleon's Cavalry after Jena and Austerlitz.
Battle of Friedland.

*The list is, of course, not complete, but included are those names which appear to be generally best known.

† The list is, of course, by no means complete, but included are those names and those battles or campaigns which appear to be most generally known in the United States. In the American Civil War, while cavalry was very active in carrying out its typical missions and particularly in raids, and while it also engaged in many independent fights and skirmishes, the principal combat elements in all of the major campaigns and battles (except Appomattox) were infantry.

Pursuit to Appomattox.
Palestine (Allenby).
Vittorio Veneto.
Salonica (Gambetta's pursuit to Uskub).
The defense of Moscow and Stalingrad (World War II).
The delaying action of the 26th U. S. Cav. (P. S.) on
Bataan peninsula, P. I. (World War II).

20. Fort Riley, Kansas.

21. Pinerolo and Tor di Quinto (advanced).

22. Saumur.

23. Hannover.

24. Weedon.

25. Vienna.

26. Tennyson's "The Charge of the Light Brigade."

27. Thirteen: The 2nd through 12th, 14th and 26th (P. S.).

28. Two, the 1st and 2nd.

29. None.

30. 5th, 7th, 8th, and 12th.

31. It fought dismounted as light infantry, distinguishing itself
    in the Southwest Pacific on the Admiralty Islands and the
    Philippines. It was first in Manila and first in Tokyo.

32. The McClellan saddle.

33. It is, in contrast, in the nature of a "flat" or "English" saddle
    with extended panels. It is frequently referred to as a
    Saumur saddle. Officially it is an officer's field saddle.

34. Approximately 11,000; exactly 11,216 under the Sept. 1944
    T/O.

35. Approximately 1,500; exactly 1,530.

36. 7 officers and 166 men; a total of 173.

37. 1 officer and 28 men; a total of 29.

38. A company.

39. A battery.

40. The squadron.

41. To provide a mobile combat element, which in cooperation with other arms, conducts such operations as utilize its essential characteristic of mobility. Usual are: Reconnaissance; counter reconnaissance; advance, rear and flank guard; raiding; exploitation of victories (pursuit); the seizing of ground and holding it until infantry arrives; delaying action, etc.

42. Unusual battle mobility combined with fire power.

43. A new, young, or "recruit" horse; one not yet trained to the prescribed standard, or finally assigned as a trooper's mount.

44. Generally half (or more) Thoroughbred. Usually by Thoroughbred sires out of light or medium weight riding horse mares of the Thoroughbred type, and with a good infusion of that blood.

45. By purchase through remount agents, largely in the western and southern states. Usually horses sired by Government stallions.

46. During recent years it has averaged $163.60; the price has never exceeded $200.00. No mounts were purchased by the Army during 1946.

47. About 15.2 hands.

48. About 1,000 pounds.

49. By the Preston Brand on the neck.

50. About 65 pounds.

51. On the saddle—in a pommel roll, a cantle roll, and in two saddle bags.

52. 250 pounds, although usually it does not exceed 200 pounds.

53. The rifle and the pistol.

54. The light machine gun, heavy machine gun, 37 mm gun (one pounder), .50 caliber air-cooled machine gun (anti-tank), 81 mm mortar, carbine, sub-machine gun (Tommy gun), and rocket launcher ("bazooka").

55. 100 miles by the Cavalry School Brigade, Fort Riley, Kansas, in the Spring of 1931 and again in the Spring of 1932.

56. Thirty-five miles.

57. 6 miles per hour.

58. The walk and trot.

59. Four miles per hour.

60. Nine miles per hour.

61. Twelve miles per hour.

62. Sixteen or more miles per hour.

63. Thirty minutes.

64. (Roughly trot 6 and walk 4 or 3.) Walk 5; trot, 6, walk 3; trot 6 and walk 4 three times; trot 6, walk 3; lead 2; halt 5.

65. At the opposite end of the line of troopers' tents (troop streets) from the kitchens and officers' tents.

66. He is directly responsible for the care of the animals, stables, picket line, forage, and public property pertaining to them for his organization, and for the supervision and control of all men working in or assigned to the stables of his organization.

67. Maj. Gen. John K. Herr.

68. Maj. Gen. Willard A. Holbrook.

69. Six. Generals Samuel B. M. Young, Adna R. Chaffee, Jay Franklin Bell, Hugh L. Scott, John J. Pershing, Malin Craig.

70. About 1,600 on October 1, 1946. At the peak of the war in 1944 it had 21,000, largely in the China-Burma-India Theater, in Italy and the Alps.

71. By purchase from private breeders. The Army helps by providing farmers with suitable jacks.

72. They are used primarily as pack animals in units trained to operate in mountainous and other difficult country. They are also used as dray animals in the normal "housekeeping" of posts, camps and stations.

73. "Horse-Mechanized" regiments, one squadron horse mounted, moving in eight horse motor trailers, the other mechanized with motor cycles, scout cars and light tanks. Headquarters and "spare parts" were entrucked or otherwise motorized.

74. They were designated GROUPS (e.g. The 3rd Cavalry *Group* instead of Regiment) with a small mobile headquarters to which a varying number of squadrons might be assigned for a limited or indefinite period. Fixed assignment of squadrons to groups was abolished, the squadron, rather than the regiment, became the administrative unit and squadrons were numbered consecutively.

75. (a) Mechanized regiments or groups; (b) Armored regiments; and (c) Infantry. (The 5th, 7th, 8th and 12th Regiments of the 1st Cavalry Division, although not actually designated infantry, were equipped, trained and partially organized and fought as infantry. The designation of the Division was changed to 1st Cavalry Division, *Special*.

76. Generally Field Artillery.

77. Three.

78. (a) Fort Reno, Oklahoma; (b) Fort Robinson, Nebraska; (c) Front Royal, Virginia.

79. The Quartermaster Corps. (The operation was basically one of procurement and supply. Most of the officers active in the depots were, however, former cavalrymen.)

80. The cavalry reconnaissance troop, mechanized.

A Test of Horsemanship
and Horsemastership

The following test is designed to set a high—but, with proper instruction, easily obtainable—standard of knowledge and accomplishment. It seems reasonable that anyone who would be considered a horseman or horsewoman should be able to pass such a test with a high score.

The outline lends itself to instruction and testing in several phases or steps. The mounted portion may, of course, precede the dismounted; and the order of dismounted instruction and testing is immaterial.

A. DISMOUNTED

1. NOMFNCLATURE: Bring in a horse:

   a. Point out 16 parts of this horse.

   b. Point to the following:
   Muzzle, hocks, loins, fetlock, cannons, knees, elbow, withers, croup, dock, forearm, point of the shoulder, coronet, gaskin, frog, pastern, bars of the jaw, stifle, chestnuts, poll.

2. TYPES AND CONFORMATION: Bring in horses of whatever types are available. Then for each ask:

   a. What type of horse is this?

   b. "Fault" him. (Point out his defects in relation to the characteristic conformation and quality of his type). Include at least: Head, eyes, neck, shoulder, withers, back, pasterns, hoofs, height and weight.

3. COLORS AND MARKINGS: Bring in horses of varied colors and markings.

   a. Have the individual name, or each of the group write, the *color* of each horse. If any of the following colored horses are not present have students describe them: Black, brown, bay, dark chestnut, light chestnut, grey, piebald, skewbald, blue roan, red roan.

   b. Have the individual describe, or each of the group write, the distinctive *markings* of each horse. If any of the following are not present, have students describe them: Blaze, race, star, snip, flecks, dapples, stockings, Preston brand, other brands.

4. RECOGNITION OF COMMON DISEASES AND FAULTS. If available, bring in a horse or horses with common diseases and defects; if none is available, bring in any horse.

   a. Point to the location and indicate the nature of the following: Curb, spavin, splint, sidebone, ringbone, thrush, capped hock, ophthalmia, thoroughpin, windpuffs, wind colic.

   b. Describe what is meant by: Cowhocked, swaybacked, tied in below the knee, ewe-necked, star gazing, herring gutted, goose rumped, forging, Roman nosed, splayfooted.

5. AGE. If available, bring in horses of the following ages: 2 to 4, 5 to 7, 8 to 9, 10 to 14, 15 to 20.

   a. What is the age of each of these horses?

     (1) Why do you think so?

   b. What in general is the characteristic appearance of the teeth of a horse that is:

     4 years old?　　6 years old?　　8 years old?

     10 years old?　　15 years old?　　20 years old?

6. STABLE MANAGEMENT: Bring in a horse; provide a section of picket line, stable ring, bridle, saddle and cleaning material for horse and tack.

a. Have student demonstrate:
   (1) How to brush the near side.
   (2) How to brush the off side.
   (3) The use of a rubber.
   (4) The use of a scraper.
   (5) The use of a hoof pick.
   (6) The use of the comb on the tail.
b. Where should a curry comb *not* be used?
c. Indicate how a twitch is used.
d. Hobble the horse.
e. Tie the horse
   (1) To the picket line,
   (2) To the ring.
f. Pick up
   (1) The horse's near forefoot,
   (2) Off hindfoot.
g. Approximately what daily quantity of each of the following would you feed a middle weight riding horse in good condition, working regularly: (1) Oats? (2) Hay? (3) Bran? (4) Salt? (5) Greens? (6) Corn?
h. How much straw bedding should a horse have, the first time new bedding is used?
i. Is fresh straw or old straw better for bedding? Why?
j. How is a bran mash made? How often is it fed?
k. Where a trough is used, in general, how many times a day should a horse be watered? At what times? Just before or after feeding?
l. Approximately how often should a horse be shod?
m. If the time for a horse to be reshod arrives, but his shoes are not worn, what should be done?
n. What is the essence of a good stable?
o. Demonstrate how to clean
   (1) A bridle,

(2) A saddle.

p. Name the parts of
(1) The bridle,
(2) The saddle.

7. BRIDLING AND SADDLING: Have a horse in his stall, haltered and tied and necessary tack (Pelham bit) at hand, the head stall, cavesson and girth *incorrectly* adjusted, the curb chain hooked on both sides, stirrup irons down.

a. Bridle and saddle this horse. (Check that curb chain is released before bridling, manner of opening mouth, proper adjustments, etc.)

b. Assume you have come in from an hour's normal riding: Untack this horse, put him in his stall, place the tack properly in the tack room.

B. MOUNTED HORSEMANSHIP

1. Mount. (Check for tightened near rein, correctness, alacrity and ease.)

2. Shorten the off stirrup one hole without removing the foot from the stirrup.

3. Tighten the girth while in the saddle.

4. Dismount.

5. WALK—Halt, Walk, Figure 8, Halt, Back.

6. TROT—Walk, Halt, Trot, Figure 8, Change diagonals; Slow trot without stirrups (in a figure 8).

7. CANTER (Right lead)—Trot, Canter (left lead), Walk, Canter (right lead), Halt. Figure 8 (check correctness of leads), Release stirrups and regain stirrups on command while cantering a figure 8, Halt.
Have rider canter in a straight line, naming the lead on which he will depart and then change leads.

8. GALLOP to a designated point, turn sharply about, right handed; gallop to the starting point, turn sharply about left handed; gallop on to a designated point and halt abruptly.

9. JUMP 2½ feet, twice (check form, control of horse, etc.)

NOTE: A thirteen-year-old boy who had not had previous experience, after about four hours' instruction a week, over a six months' period, passed this test with a score of 96 per cent.

Outline for a Mounted Drill

OUTLINE FOR A MOUNTED DRILL

In a Riding Hall—Consuming Approximately Thirty Minutes

Fall In.
Count fours.
Anyone who feels incapable of riding at No. 1 or 4, change
  positions.

Fours right, *March.*
Column right, *March.*
Column of twos, *March.*
Column of troopers, *March.*
Column of fours, *March.*
Column of troopers, *March.*

Trot, *March.*
Column of twos, *March.*
Column of fours, *March.*
Column of troopers, *March.*
Change hands.
Walk, *March.*
Release stirrups.
Slow trot, *March* (Once around ring).
Walk, *March.*
Half-turn.
Troopers circle to the left.
Half-turn and reverse.
Half-turn.

219

Troopers circle to the right.

Half-turn and reverse.

From front to rear count *threes*.

Take stirrups.

Trot, *March*.

By threes, by the left flank, *March* (Track Right) (At one end of hall).

By threes, by the right flank, *March* (Track Left) (The other end of hall).

Column of fours, *March*.

Walk, *March*.

Fours left, *March*.

Troop, *Halt*.

Column of fours from the right, Trot *March*.

Column right, *March*.

Column of twos, *March*.

Column of troopers, *March*.

(At the middle of one end of the ring) Column Right, *March*.

Troopers left and right (at opposite end of ring).

Columns half left and half right (when leading troopers reach end of ring on each side. This produces a cross-over or criss-cross in the center of the ring).

Columns half left and half right (Double back).

Column of twos (At end of ring).

Twos, left and right.

(Twos) Column half left and half right (Criss-cross).

(Twos) Columns half left and half right (Double back).

Column of fours (At end of ring).

Fours, left and right.

(Fours) Column half left and half right (Criss-cross).

(Fours) Column half left and half right (Double back).

(Caution—"Even fours left, odd fours right".)

Line, *March* (At end of ring).

Walk, *March*.

Troop, *Halt.*

Lead out from the right and ride at will—cool your horses.

NOTE: If desired, with an advanced group, movements indicated at a walk may be at a trot and those indicated at a trot may be at a canter (collected gallop).

Your Score

The following table is provided to facilitate converting the NUMBER of questions answered correctly in each of the twelve sections to a percentage SCORE. The score for the total of all sections may be computed by averaging the scores for each section, i.e., adding the twelve individual scores and dividing this sum by twelve.

SCORING TABLE FOR EACH SECTION

NUMBER OF CORRECT ANSWERS	YOUR (HIS, HER) SCORE	NUMBER OF CORRECT ANSWERS	YOUR (HIS, HER) SCORE
1	1	21	26
2	2	22	27
3	4	23	29
4	5	24	30
5	6	25	31
6	7	26	32
7	9	27	34
8	10	28	35
9	11	29	36
10	12	30	37
11	14	31	39
12	15	32	40
13	16	33	41
14	17	34	42
15	18	35	44
16	20	36	45
17	21	37	46
18	22	38	47
19	24	39	49
20	25	40	50

SCORING TABLE FOR EACH SECTION

Number of Correct Answers	Your (His, Her) Score	Number of Correct Answers	Your (His, Her) Score
41	51	61	76
42	52	62	77
43	54	63	79
44	55	64	80
45	56	65	81
46	57	66	82
47	59	67	84
48	60	68	85
49	61	69	86
50	62	70	87
51	64	71	89
52	65	72	90
53	66	73	91
54	67	74	92
55	69	75	94
56	70	76	95
57	71	77	96
58	72	78	97
59	74	79	99
60	75	80	100